THE ILLUSTRATED GUIDE TO
HYDROPONICS

*This book is dedicated to my
grandchildren*

THE ILLUSTRATED GUIDE TO
HYDROPONICS

DUDLEY HARRIS

NH
NEW HOLLAND

Author's Acknowledgements

My grateful thanks are due to the following individuals, firms and institutions for permission to take photographs on their premises: Mr Michael Albeldas of Philflora for those on pp. 50 & 52; Mr Mark Bilton, the pioneer of GFT, for those on pp. 21, 22, 74; The Director, Booysens Nursery, Pretoria, for those on pp. 15, 27 (top), 40 & 75 (bottom); Mr Tony Horsfall of ESCOM Nursery, Johannesburg, for those on pp. 31, 37 (bottom), 39 (bottom), 73 & cover (pH meter); Mr Harry Stephan for those on pp. 43 & 68 (top); Mr Ernest Thomson of Plants Cape for those on pp. 8, 10 & 39 (all except bottom); WJR Plants for those on the title page and pp. 65 & 67 (top); The Director of The National Botanical Institute, Kirstenbosch, for that on page 47. Sincere thanks are also due to the following individuals who so willingly responded to my request for photographs: Professor Peter Maree for those on pp. 20 (top), 23, 33, 44, 54, 56, 76, 77; Mr Warren Nelson of Starke Ayres for that on page 48.

I must also mention the wonderful co-operation I received from Struik's hard-working team. Thank you to everyone involved in producing this book, and to Elizabeth Frost and Lauren Morris in particular. Finally, thanks to the principal photographer, Jackie Murray, whose efforts are recorded under the photographic credits below, and to Alix Gracie for all the magnificent drawings in the book.

First published in the UK in 1994 by
New Holland (Publishers) Ltd
37 Connaught Street, London W2 2AZ

ISBN 1 85368 307 8

EDITOR Elizabeth Frost
DESIGNER Lauren Morris
COVER DESIGN Janice Evans and Lauren Morris
PHOTOGRAPHY AND PICTURE RESEARCH Jackie Murray
ILLUSTRATIONS Alix Gracie

Typeset by Struik DTP
Reproduction by Unifoto (Pty) Ltd, Cape Town
Printed and bound in Singapore by Tien Wah Press (Pte.), Ltd

CONTENTS

PREFACE

People have always had an innate desire to grow plants. This has probably arisen from the necessity to supplement their diet with fresh, vitamin-rich vegetables, or the attraction of an aesthetically pleasing environment adorned with flowers, trees and ornamental shrubs.

In the Bible we read, 'Now the Lord God had planted a garden in the east, in Eden . . . trees that were pleasing to the eye and good for food' (*Genesis 2:v8,9*).

Among the staple foods of that time were the wild olive, fig, date, fruits of the vine and a variety of cereals, while among the decorative plants were the blossom of the almond, the scarlet flowers of the pomegranate, and the 'lilies of the field' (possibly the yellow chrysanthemum). The cedars of Lebanon and the oaks on Mount Carmel are legend. Equally familiar is the Egyptian papyrus that grew in swampy areas of the Nile delta where water-borne nutrients proliferated to feed the plants. This is a good example of hydroponics occurring in nature, and provides a useful introduction to our subject.

Hydroponics – the very word seems to conjure up an image of mystery. This book has been written in an attempt to clearly explain the theory and practice of, in the words of Chapter One, 'What is hydroponics?'. The text contains copious practical details, which are clearly illustrated by photographs and diagrams.

My first book, *Hydroponics: The Complete Guide to Gardening Without Soil* (New Holland Publishers, 1994), now in its seventh edition, was divided into three parts. The first, for the prospective hydroponic grower with little or no previous knowledge of the subject; the second, for the more technically minded reader; and the third, for the commercial grower. *The Illustrated Guide to Hydroponics* has been specially written for the first-time grower who would like to grow indoors or on the verandah, as well as for the home grower wanting to produce fresh salad vegetables or flowers in a limited area outside the flat or home.

Many books on hydroponics are rather intimidating as they can be frighteningly technical. It is, however, quite possible to grow plants successfully by this method with very little or no technical knowledge. The aim of *The Illustrated Guide to Hydroponics* is to help you to do just this.

Valuable practical information for the ordinary gardener who has no special interest in hydroponics is also contained between these pages. For example, Chapter Ten, 'Pests and diseases', presents a unique scheme for eliminating or, at worst, keeping these enemies under control.

It is my sincere hope that those who wish to get going with this fascinating form of gardening will be better equipped to do so after reading this book.

Dudley Harris

Dudley Harris

PLEASE NOTE
- All weights and measures used in this book are based on the metric system. For those readers more familiar with Imperial measurements, approximate equivalents have been provided in brackets.
- Diagrams are provided to assist the reader to better understand the text and have not necessarily, in all cases, been drawn exactly to scale.
- Brand names appear in one or two of the photographs in the book. This in no way implies endorsement of a brand name or approval over any similar products.

CHAPTER ONE

WHAT IS HYDROPONICS?

The word 'water' is the key to the definition of hydroponics. All methods of growing plants by hydroponics involve the use of water. The term, which is derived from two Greek words – *hydro*, meaning 'water' and *ponos*, meaning 'labour', or literally, 'working in water' – was coined by the pioneer of commercial hydroponics as we know it today, Dr W. F. Gericke of California in the 1930s.

A modern definition might run like this: *Hydroponics is the science and art of growing plants in a solid medium other than soil, irrigated with the essential plant nutrient elements dissolved in water.* Hydroponics also includes growing plants – without a solid medium – in water in which fertilizers have been dissolved.

Although the practice is also known as 'aggregate culture', 'soil-less culture', 'nutriculture' or even 'chemiculture', Dr Gericke's term is used so universally that *all* methods of growing plants without soil are loosely referred to as 'hydroponics'. We shall therefore use this word throughout to denote *any* method of growing plants without soil.

The essential difference between growing plants in soil and growing them hydroponically is that the latter method involves no organic matter or use of earth. This has important implications for farming and horti-culture in general, as crops can be grown on virtually any vacant space, whether it be rock, swamp or desert, though of course the vital ingredient is water.

This method also has great advantages for the householder wishing to grow either fresh vegetables or orna-mentals indoors or outside – these will be discussed more fully later in this chapter.

Palms grown by hydroculture

A BRIEF HISTORY

Unwittingly, people have been prac-tising hydroponics since Biblical times. A good example is one of the ancient wonders of the world, the Hanging Gardens of Babylon, which may have been the first attempt to grow plants without soil.

The first recorded experiment to determine what ingredients made plants grow is attributed to John Woodward in England in 1699, though it is very likely that experi-ments had been done before this time. Woodward cultivated plants in water to which different amounts of soil had been added. He con-cluded that the vital elements need-ed by plants for healthy growth were derived from the soil extract-ed by the water, rather than from the water itself.

Woodward's research was limited by the equipment at his disposal and it was only during the nineteenth century, by which time scientific research methods had improved, that further progress was made. In France, De Saussure (1804) and Boussingault (1851–6) collectively illustrated that, in order to grow, plants require elements obtained from soil, in addition to water and gases from the atmosphere.

The well-documented experiments of the two German plant scientists, Sachs (1860) and Knop (1861–5), were the real basis of hydroponics as we know it today. They made synthetic solutions of the essential plant nutrients. Included in these solutions were salts such as potas-sium nitrate, calcium sulphate, mag-nesium sulphate, calcium phosphate and ferrous phosphate, thus proving that nitrogen, phosphorus, potas-sium, calcium, magnesium, sulphur and iron were essential elements for plant growth. Manganese was also included, but not enough was known at the time about the other essential trace elements, so these were omitted. The composition of the nutrient solutions used by these men was published and may be used to this day, provided that cer-tain additions are made.

Much research was undertaken by scientists, mainly in the United States, around the beginning of the century. Their work resulted in the publication of nutrient formulae as well as methods of growing. By this time the universities were well involved in research; the work of Alice and Robert Withrow at Purdue University in the United States in the 1940s gave us the sub-irrigation method of hydroponics, which they called 'nutriculture'.

The hydroponic method may be used to beautify any office foyer

The commercial development of hydroponics began in California in the 1930s with the work of Dr W.F. Gericke. He set up large tanks filled with nutrient solutions, in which he grew tomatoes. The warm, sunny Californian climate was certainly a help and he was spectacularly successful. Tomato yields and quality were outstanding. The plants grew to heights of over 7 m (23 ft), making it necessary to use ladders to pick the crop. Journalists of the day exaggerated the facts out of all proportion, and all over America people were mixing fertilizer chemicals and waiting for the magic to begin! Failure to grow similar crops by these hopeful amateurs caused water culture – the true hydroponics – to be regarded as the big let-down! This was somewhat unfortunate as it set back the development of hydroponics in no small measure. However, the momentum was not entirely lost, and research into the subject at universities continued to be fairly active in the 1930s.

The outbreak of the Second World War gave a considerable boost to the practical development of hydroponics. This was largely due to the efforts of the American armed forces stationed in the Pacific region, who grew vegetables hydroponically for daily eating. It is recorded that on Wake Island, for example, 11 m² (13 sq yd) of water culture yielded 15 kg (33 lb) of tomatoes, 20 heads of lettuce, 9 kg (20 lb) of string beans, 7 kg (15 lb) of vegetable marrow and 20 kg (44 lb) of sweetcorn weekly. Generally, though, plants were grown in solid media – the most favoured being gravel – into which were pumped the dissolved plant nutrient elements.

At present, large and small installations exist in practically every country of the world, in environments ranging from the arid desertlands of Saudi Arabia, to the frigid climates of Scandinavia. Surprisingly, the largest area cultivated hydroponically is to be found in one of the smallest

Begonia, Caladium *and* Dracaena *species contribute to an attractive indoor decor*

countries in Europe, The Netherlands, where installations in which both vegetable and floral crops are grown, cover a total area of over 3,600 ha (8,895 acres).

ADVANTAGES OF HYDROPONICS

It may well occur to the reader that, rather than bother with containers, growing media and chemical nutrients, it would be much easier to prepare an area of soil, plant the desired seeds, cuttings or seedlings and leave the rest to nature. This would be so, assuming that a good soil was available, and that the grower was prepared to weed, cultivate and fertilize the soil.

However, the list of advantages of growing by the hydroponic method is impressive, making it worth considering as an alternative.

Some of the advantages of hydroponic growing appear in the following list, and are discussed in further detail in the next few pages.

- versatility
- better control
- no cultivation
- larger yields
- uniform results
- cleanliness
- less labour
- almost no weeds
- ease of starting new plants
- a means of upgrading poor plants
- an educational hobby

Though many of these advantages apply more particularly to the commercial grower, the small-scale grower – and this includes those wanting to grow in window-boxes and beds – will also benefit.

A more detailed examination of these advantages will convince the reader of the merits of growing plants by the hydroponic method. Experienced growers will endorse every one of these claims!

Versatilty

In most urban areas there is a vast and ever-growing population of flat-dwellers to whom hydroponics is especially suited. Flower boxes filled with a suitable growing medium and watered with nutrient will grow almost anything the flat-dweller desires. Indoor gardens, window-sill arrangements, balcony vegetables, even herbs for the kitchen – all are possible with hydroponics.

Special emphasis must be placed on the many and varied indoor plants that one can grow by *hydroculture* – a technique of growing in clay pellets. This is the subject of a later chapter (see page 37).

Better control

Every grower knows the benefits of growing plants in a rich soil of the correct tilth. But more often than not this is the ideal, which is usually not easily attainable.

Many natural soils lack one or other of the essential plant nutrients. Phosphorus, one of the big six of the macro-(major) elements, is a good example. Some soils are so deficient in this element that healthy plant growth is not possible. And so the grower must fertilize the soil with superphosphate, a form of calcium phosphate. In a similar way, potassium sulphate or chloride is added to increase the potassium content; ammonium sulphate, nitrate or urea for nitrogen, and so on.

The hydroponic method of growing automatically guarantees a balanced nutrient solution that can be controlled to a fine degree and altered to suit the needs of a particular plant. For example, in general, leaf crops prefer more nitrogen, and root crops more phosphorus. In hydroponic gardening it is comparatively easy to provide more or less of any of the nutrient elements.

Controlling pH levels – or the degree of acidity – in the soil is another potential problem area. Imagine that you wish to grow acid-loving plants such as azaleas or proteas in an alkaline soil. It is by no means easy, and certainly costly –

especially on a commercial scale – to reduce the pH of an alkaline soil from, say, 8.0 to 5.0. Using the hydroponic system it is easy to maintain, within limits, any desired pH value of a nutrient solution and, if necessary, to decrease or increase this value for optimum growing conditions.

No cultivation

The drudgery of digging, hoeing and raking soil is virtually unknown in hydroponics. The aim of these tasks is to provide aeration, without which healthy growth is impossible. The advantage of hydroponic growing is that the durable growing media used not only provide anchorage for the roots, but also allow vital aeration, and moisture and nutrient retention.

Gravel is an example of a growing medium that meets all these criteria, with the added benefit that it affords root systems a 'bonus' supply of air when irrigated from below or sub-irrigated, as it is popularly known (see page 44).

Larger yields

When the subject of hydroponics is mentioned, the uninformed reader automatically assumes that extraordinary yields are to be expected. Although there is no hard evidence to support the theory that growing by hydroponics yields higher and better crops than those grown in good soil or peat by experts using the best methods, the possibilities of failure to reach the potential yield in soil culture are greater. Therefore, amateurs might well find that hydroponics gives them better yields than more traditional methods.

With most crops it can be conservatively estimated that, on a commercial scale, the hydroponic method will produce from two to four times the yield expected in soil. The home grower growing tomatoes, for example, should consistently crop 6–9 kg (13–20 lb) per plant.

Uniform results

The main aim in hydroponics, which is a scientific method of growing, is to standardize irrigation and nutritional cycles as well as to choose a stable growing medium. This methodical approach tends to result in floral or vegetable crop uniformity, an invaluable merit for the commercial grower. Contrast this with growing in soil, with its often great diversity of physical and chemical properties.

When plants are grown in greenhouses with climatic control the factor of uniformity can be increased to an even finer degree, resulting in near factory production of crops.

Cleanliness

When manures and other animal excreta are used to fertilize soil there is a very real danger of spreading disease. This is particularly pertinent to the vegetable crops that grow close to the soil surface, such as lettuce, spinach and watercress. Dysentery, gastro-enteritis and other stomach complaints are just some of the illnesses that can be contracted as a result of eating contaminated vegetables.

It was largely for this reason that the United States Army stationed in Japan established a 22 ha (54 acre) hydroponic installation. Many years of unsanitary cultivation had left the soil so full of disease-bearing organisms that the troops were forbidden to eat fresh soil-grown vegetables. The use of sterilized gravel and nutrient solutions solved the problem completely.

Less labour

In most manufacturing procedures, and this includes agriculture, the labour costs are generally the biggest factor. Agriculture is indeed a labour-intensive activity and we see constant attempts to mechanize wherever possible.

The same is true of horticulture. With hydroponics, however, digging, fertilizing and irrigating can be integrated into one mechanical operation using gravel, an electric pump and a time-clock. This is as near to automatic gardening as one can get and is one of the most attractive attributes of the hydroponic method.

The advantage of this for the home grower is that it is actually possible to go on vacation, return home, and pick the flowers or fruit from your hydroponic garden . . . all you need is a friend to adjust the pH of your nutrient solution occasionally!

Almost no weeds

More often than not, weeds are soil-borne. As hydroponic growing requires sterile growing media, this source is eliminated. Should a few wind-blown seeds take root in the growing medium, they can be very easily dealt with.

Imagine gardening with one of its major irritations virtually eliminated!

Ease of starting new plants

It is simplicity itself for the hydroponic grower to raise seedlings in a growing medium such as vermiculite or rockwool cubes.

A big advantage of using this method is that it is not necessary to prepare a special soil for seedlings, and once raised, the seedlings can be transplanted with almost no shock and resultant set-back.

A means of upgrading poor plants

Another advantage of the hydroponic method is that it facilitates the revitalizing of poor, even unhealthy, plants. As long as no irreversible damage has been done, poorly grown plants, transplanted into a hydroponic medium, can be transformed into sound plants, even if they never quite catch up with those that had a healthy start.

An educational hobby

Hydroponics can be educational as well as a relaxing, enjoyable hobby. From the beginning of recorded experiments plant physiologists have used their observations of plants growing hydroponically to unfold the mysteries of plant growth, and it offers the hobbyist the same opportunity. No one will deny its value to scholars and students seeking to learn something about plants and their growth. Put into practice, terms such as 'pH value', 'growing medium' and 'trace elements' soon take on a new meaning for the student.

Hydroponics can be a splendid hobby for anyone from eight to 80. It also affords gardening opportunities for the physically handicapped, which conventional gardening methods preclude.

DISADVANTAGES OF HYDROPONICS

Surely, the reader may ask, there must be some disadvantages to this method of growing.

Here are some of these:

• The commercial grower may well complain of the high cash outlay for the construction of concrete tanks in the gravel sub-irrigation system, and for the necessary ancillary equipment, such as electric pumps, automatic irrigation systems and reservoirs. This limits commercial growing to crops commanding premium prices on the market. Costs, however, can be considerably trimmed by using overhead drip irrigation into plastic growing bags.

The above objections would not apply to the home grower, who would undoubtedly operate on a very much smaller scale.

• There is a perception among lay people that hydroponics is somewhat technical, requiring a knowledge of chemistry. While it is undoubtedly

true that anyone practising hydroponic growing on a commercial scale would benefit from a basic knowledge of agricultural chemistry and even plant physiology, the same does not apply to home growing. The reason for this is that commercial plant nutrient mixtures are readily available. These contain all the necessary macro- and micro-elements (see Appendix 2) in a balanced, water-soluble powder form. For general use, one simply dissolves the powder in water and applies the solution to the growing medium. This eliminates the need for stocks of chemicals, expensive scales and chemical understanding.

INTERNATIONAL SOCIETY FOR SOILLESS CULTURE (ISOSC)

Established in 1955, the International Society for Soilless Culture (ISOSC) is an international, non-profit, non-governmental organization devoted to the world-wide promotion of research and practical application of soilless culture. It operates as an information centre and the Secretariat in The Netherlands, or its official representatives on different continents, provide technical information on hydroponics. An international congress is held every three or four years, and the proceedings thereof are published.

Another very important task of ISOSC is the compilation of a bibliography on the literature of hydroponics (see page 77).

The present Secretary/Treasurer of ISOSC is Ing. A. A. Steiner, a name virtually synonomous with ISOSC, whose untiring efforts have been largely responsible for its continuing success. The postal address of the Secretariat is:
ISOSC
PO Box 52
6700AB, Wageningen
The Netherlands.

CHAPTER TWO

PLANT COMPOSITION
AND GROWTH

Before learning about soilless plant growth the reader should have some understanding of how plants grow in their normal environment – the soil. This will provide an introduction to simple soil science.

To appreciate this, a basic knowledge of what constitutes a plant is the first requirement.

PLANT COMPOSITION

A cursory inspection of a dicotyledonous plant shows that it consists of three main parts, which are illustrated in Fig. 1, namely:

• the leaves
• the stem
• the root system

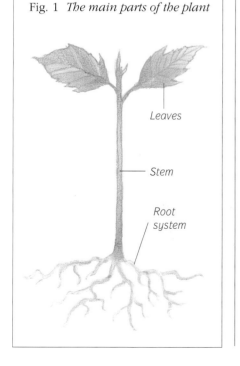

Fig. 1 *The main parts of the plant*

Leaves

Stem

Root system

In addition to these, one can also observe in the mature plant the flower for reproducing the species.

The basic building bricks, or cells, of a plant may be examined under a microscope. Certain of these plant cells are specialized for conducting water or storing foodstuffs.

All cells are filled with a jelly-like living material known as *protoplasm*, which is structurally very complex. This consists mainly of the protein-like *cytoplasm* and the *nucleus* or cell control centre.

The leaves

A major difference between plants and animals is the fact that the former can manufacture their own foodstuffs from simple substances. The leaves are the factory of the plant, where the primary foodstuffs are manufactured.

Using the energy provided by sunlight in a process known as *photosynthesis*, carbon dioxide from the air (only 0.03 per cent by volume) combines initially with hydrogen derived from water, to form simple sugars such as glucose, for example. From this, more complex sugars, starches, acids and proteins are produced.

The remarkable green substance responsible for photosynthesis is *chlorophyll*, a complex of light-absorbing pigments.

The other important role played by the leaves is that of air-conditioner. By means of numerous little pores called *stomata*, usually found on the underside of the leaf, water vapour evaporates into the atmosphere on a hot day, thereby cooling the plant. This is known as *transpiration*, and is analogous to animal perspiration.

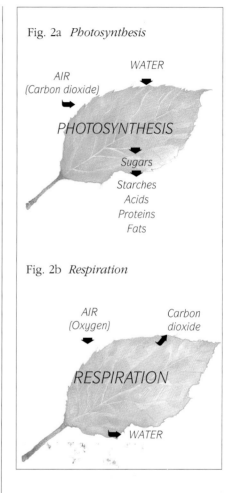

Fig. 2a *Photosynthesis*

WATER

AIR
(Carbon dioxide)

PHOTOSYNTHESIS

Sugars

Starches
Acids
Proteins
Fats

Fig. 2b *Respiration*

AIR
(Oxygen)

Carbon
dioxide

RESPIRATION

WATER

Stomata also allow the diffusion of carbon dioxide and oxygen into and out of the leaf.

Respiration, similar to our breathing, is the term given to the process whereby sugars are broken down by oxygen into their original components of carbon dioxide and water, releasing energy used in growth. This is the exact opposite of photosynthesis. Respiration takes place at a slow but steady rate all the time, whereas photosynthesis occurs only in the presence of light of sufficient quantity and quality.

The stem

The stem, which is the least specialized part of the plant:

• connects the roots with the leaves;
• conducts water and nutrients from the roots to the leaves;
• conducts sugars, and so on, downwards from the leaves, where they are produced, to the roots, and
• sometimes serves as a storage reservoir for plant foods.

The flower

Like most living organisms, the plant has male and female parts, which are housed in the flower. The petals form the *corolla*, at the base of which is the *ovary*, usually positioned in the middle. The female receptive organ is the *stigma*, which is attached to the end of an elongated tube called the *style*.

The male portion of the plant consists of the *stamens*, which produce *pollen* in the boat-shaped *anthers*. After bursting out of the anthers the pollen grains attach themselves to the stigma, resulting finally in the fertilization of the ovary. After enlarging, the ovary emerges as a fruit containing the seeds for the next generation.

Most plants, for example the

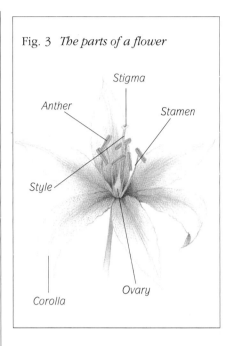

Fig. 3 *The parts of a flower*

Stigma

Anther

Stamen

Style

Ovary

Corolla

tomato, have male and female parts in the same flower. Some, like the cucumber, have separate male and female flowers on the same plant. Others, of which the pawpaw and holly are examples, have male and female flowers on different plants.

Reproduction may also take place *asexually;* this occurs when species are propagated by means of leaf, stem or root cuttings.

The root system

Roots serve the very important purpose of anchoring the plant in the soil or soilless growing medium. The other vital function of the root system is to absorb water and mineral salts, which together make up the soil solution.

Most roots branch profusely, resulting in the formation of secondary and tertiary rootlets, each covered – near the tip – with thousands of root hairs. These fine hairs have *semi-permeable* cell walls. This means that they selectively allow certain minerals as well as water to pass through them. The fine rootlets are in intimate contact with the soil particles and, by *osmosis*, absorb water when it is required by the plant. Imagine the enormous area that all the root hairs on the plant rootlets will cover when intertwined around the millions of moist particles making up the soil (see Fig. 4).

To gain a clearer understanding of the osmotic process, imagine a glass of water with one teaspoon of sugar dissolved in it. A small thimble made of parchment paper (a type of semi-permeable membrane), and filled with a strong

The reproductive parts of a flower

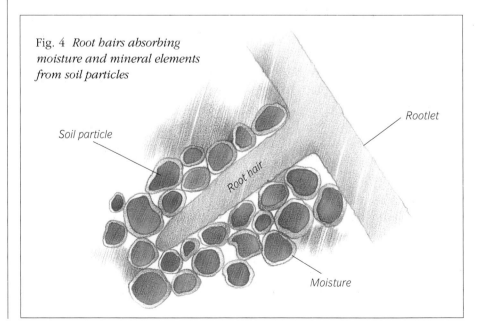

Fig. 4 *Root hairs absorbing moisture and mineral elements from soil particles*

Soil particle

Rootlet

Root hair

Moisture

Outdoor shrubs and trees in leca

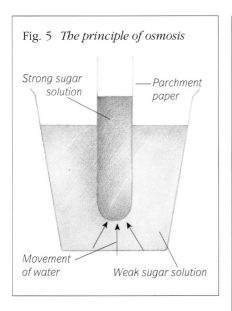

Fig. 5 *The principle of osmosis*

Strong sugar solution

—Parchment paper

Movement of water

Weak sugar solution

---

sugar solution double the concentration of that in the glass, is placed in this glass of weak sugar solution. It will be found that the water in the glass passes through the parchment paper thimble, and in so doing, dilutes the stronger solution until it is the same concentration as that in the glass (see Fig. 5).

Now imagine replacing the glass of water with a dilute soil solution, and the solution in the parchment paper thimble with the roots' cell sap. Water passes into a plant through its semi-permeable root hairs by osmosis, in exactly the same way as in the above example.

The opposite of osmosis – known as *plasmolysis* – takes place when the level of moisture in the soil becomes so low that the soil solution is more concentrated than the plant's cell sap. This causes a flow of water out of the plant via the root hairs, and wilting, which occurs as a result of the cell contracting away from its outer wall of cellulose.

SOIL

Soil, can be divided into:

• an organic part, and
• an inorganic part.

The organic part of soil is itself a rather complex mixture of many component raw materials. Plant remains and animal residues, broken down by fungal and bacterial action, make up the familiar black material or *humus*, as it is called. The function of this mixture is three-fold: to increase the water-holding capacity of the soil; to help hold inorganic plant nutrients by minute electrical charges, and to provide nitrogen, albeit in limited quantities. This is the 'living' part of the soil, and micro-organisms thrive in it.

The 'non-living' or inorganic part of the soil is represented by the broken-down rock particles. These consist largely of sand (silica) and clay (complex hydrated aluminium silicates), together with other decomposed minerals partially or wholly dissolved in the water present in the soil. This forms the *soil solution*, which contains the elements vital to plant growth.

A soil, therefore, is a mixture of decomposed organic remains with micro-organisms and chemically altered rock material, ranging in size from clays, to silt, fine sand, coarse sand and gravel. In addition to these, the important components of air and water are present.

The approximate percentage by volume of each of these constituents is represented diagrammatically in Fig. 6, although relative values will vary according to soil type.

The structure of soil is like that of crumbs, each one being surrounded by water. The spaces between the 'crumbs' contain the soil air.

Like atmospheric air, soil air is composed of 20 per cent life-giving oxygen, essential for the respiration of the plant roots and the aerobic soil organisms, and a small percentage of carbon dioxide. The formation of root hairs is largely dependent on the presence of sufficient oxygen. Different soil types hold differing amounts of air and water – because of the varying size of the 'crumbs' or soil particles – and this will also affect plant growth.

MINERAL ELEMENTS AND PLANT GROWTH

The mineral elements responsible for plant growth and development bring us to what is essentially common ground between growing in soil and hydroponics.

All the elements required by the plant for its growth are absorbed through its root system from the soil solution. (It should be noted in passing that some plants, like the leguminosae – for example, peas, beans, and so on – are able to obtain some of their nitrogen from the soil air, where nitrogen is converted to nitrates by bacteria living in nodules on the plant roots.)

The main feature of hydroponic growing is that the major and minor elements required by the plant are supplied in the form of a *nutrient solution*. This can be compared to the dilute soil solution. One of the essential differences

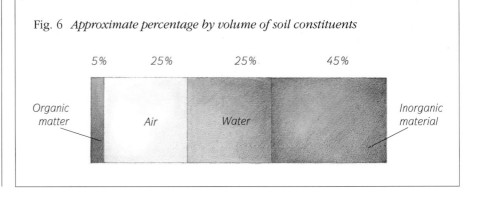

Fig. 6 *Approximate percentage by volume of soil constituents*

5%   25%   25%   45%

Organic matter   Air   Water   Inorganic material

between plants growing in soil and those grown hydroponically, therefore, is that for plants growing in soil, the minerals must be decomposed into a water-soluble form so that they are available to the plant's roots; in hydroponics, the roots are provided with a nutrient solution that is as close as possible to a good soil solution. There is therefore no apparent reason for any physiological differences between plants grown in soil and those grown hydroponically.

There are six major (or macro-) elements and some seven minor (or micro-) elements necessary for plant growth and development. The minor elements are also referred to as 'trace elements', since they are usually required in minute quantities.

The macro-elements, with their chemical symbols given in brackets, are nitrogen (N), phosphorus (P), potassium (K), calcium (Ca), magnesium (Mg) and sulphur (S).

The micro-elements are iron (Fe), manganese (Mn), boron (B), copper (Cu), zinc (Zn) and molybdenum (Mo). Chlorine (Cl) is regarded as the seventh micro-element. In addition to these, small quantities of sodium and aluminium, as well as traces of many other elements, have been found in plants, although they are not essential for plant growth.

For the last 150 years, plant scientists have been attempting to expand our knowledge of mineral element function. Today, the role played by each element in promoting plant growth is more or less known; in some cases, however, the mechanism is still somewhat obscure.

Below is a summary of some of the functions of these elements:

Macro-elements

NITROGEN is an essential component of all proteins, which is also found in chlorophyll and cytoplasm. An excess produces a lush and softish growth. A deficiency results in short stems with light green to yellow foliage and small leaves.

PHOSPHORUS is essential to all living cells and will be found in abundance in cytoplasm as well as in seeds and fruits. A lack of phosphorus results in thick, small cells and dull, bluish-green leaves with a purple tint.

POTASSIUM is essential for promoting strong growth. It is found in areas of high physiological activity, namely developing fruits and leaves. The visual symptoms of potassium deficiency are retarded growth of the terminal shoot, dull, bluish-green leaves and chlorosis (yellowing) between the leaf veins. There is also brown marginal scorching, followed by an upward curling of the leaf.

CALCIUM provides building material for cell walls, where it is found in abundance, and neutralizes organic acids. If there is a deficiency, young leaves become distorted, their tips hook back and the margins tip backwards or forwards. The growing points of the plants are often distorted or killed by a lack of calcium.

MAGNESIUM is found in smaller amounts in the plant. It is mainly concerned with the formation of chlorophyll. Deficiency symptoms are most marked on older leaves, which become mottled and yellow between the veins. Brown, dead patches develop, leading ultimately to the withering of the leaves.

SULPHUR is distributed throughout the plant in small amounts. In its organic form, sulphur is present in certain proteins and essential oils. In many ways, a deficiency in sulphur resembles a deficiency in nitrogen.

Micro-elements

IRON promotes biochemical change and is used by the plant mainly as a catalytic agent. It also plays a role in the synthesis of chlorophyll.

MANGANESE, BORON, ZINC, COPPER AND MOLYBDENUM are used by the plant as catalytic agents in various enzymatic and physiological functions.

CHLORINE in the form of the chloride ion is required for the growth and development of shoots and roots.

Water

Plant matter consists of 85–95 per cent water. At least 90 per cent of the remaining 5–15 per cent dry matter is composed of organic materials formed from carbon (C), hydrogen (H), nitrogen (N) and oxygen (O). Water (H_2O) supplies the hydrogen and oxygen, and the atmosphere gives the plant carbon, from its carbon dioxide (CO_2) content, and oxygen. The thirteen macro- and micro-elements therefore make up less than 2 per cent of the total plant.

Table 1 gives an approximate breakdown of the content of the tomato fruit, compared with that of green grass.

Table 1		
	Tomato %	Grass %
Water	95	75
Organic substances (sugars, starches, etc.)	4.2	23
Ash (mixture of inorganic elements)	0.8	2
	100	100

An organic substance is one that contains carbon. The organic matter referred to in the table are carbohydrates (sugars and starches), which are photosynthesized in the leaf from atmospheric carbon dioxide and water. These carbohydrates are, in turn, changed into further organic compounds such as proteins, fats, acids and other complex substances which are responsible for the taste of vegetables and the colour of flowers.

CHAPTER THREE

WATER CULTURE: THE TRUE HYDROPONICS

Hydroponic growing may be conveniently divided into two broad groups. The first is 'true' hydroponics, originally developed by Dr Gericke. Known as *water culture,* it involves supporting plants in a layer of suitable material and suspending this over a tank containing nutrient solution, in which the roots are immersed. Several variations based on this principle have been developed since Dr Gericke's original system. Though used in many countries on a commercial scale, these methods are not as suitable for home growing as hydroponic growing in solid media. They can, however, be practised on a small scale, and provide the ideal opportunity for the hobbyist to experiment.

The second method of hydroponic growing, which will be covered in detail in Chapter Four, involves growing plants in a solid medium other than soil, for which we use the terms *soilless* or *aggregate culture.* This method of soilless culture necessitates filling some type of container with a growing medium, planting the seeds (or transplanting seedlings) and irrigating them with the nutrient solution.

As a result of work started in the late 1960s, a modern version of water culture, more practical for raising crops on a large scale, was developed by Dr Allen Cooper at the Glasshouse Crops Research Institute, Littlehampton, England. He called this *Nutrient Film Technique,* which is commonly abbreviated to *NFT.* Large commercial installations in the UK employ this method of growing, which will be described in more detail later in this chapter.

Water culture in Nature

GENERAL CONSTRUCTION

In designing a water culture installation three criteria must be satisfied. Provision should be made for:

- support of the plants;
- aeration of the nutrient solution, and
- darkness around the root area.

The nutrient is held in a container or tank, 150–200 mm (6–8 in) in depth and of any convenient length and width, though not normally more than 1.25 m (4 ft). It can be made of glass, plastic, wood, metal or concrete, the last three of which would have to be protected by at least two coats of a bitumen paint or emulsion. Glass should be covered with black polythene or cardboard to exclude light from the root area.

A wooden tray, 5–10 mm (¼ –½ in) deep, for supporting a wire mesh is fitted to a recess at the top of the nutrient tank. The wire mesh, coated with bitumen to prevent contamination of the nutrient, is fixed to the bottom of the wooden tray. (Plastic mesh may be substituted for wire mesh, which will eliminate the need to coat with bitumen.)

Leave an air space of 12–25 mm (½ –1 in) between the bottom of the tray and the top of the nutrient solution. As the roots of the plants grow, reduce the volume of the nutrient slightly until a 50 mm (2 in) air space exists. This allows oxygen to reach the roots of the plant.

A bedding of porous material, the litter, which can be wood shavings, straw, peat moss or even rice hulls, is placed over the wire. The relative coarseness and moisture retention

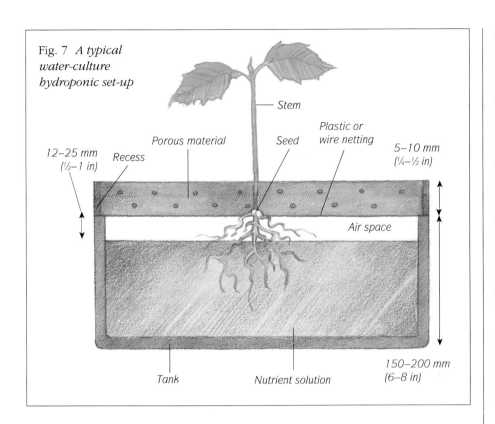

Fig. 7 *A typical water-culture hydroponic set-up*

Stem

Porous material

Seed

Plastic or wire netting

12–25 mm (½–1 in)

Recess

5–10 mm (¼–½ in)

Air space

150–200 mm (6–8 in)

Tank

Nutrient solution

cork cover – one to accommodate a plastic or glass tube for aerating the nutrient, and the other with a 'keyhole' extension for supporting the plant stem. Slide the young plant, which has been raised in another medium, into the 'keyhole' slot, using muslin, glass wool or any suitable material packed firmly around the stem to support it (see Fig. 8). A dark glass jar, a sheath of brown paper or black polythene will keep the light from the roots. However, it is not always necessary to keep the roots in the dark. Hyacinths, for example, have long been grown in special clear glass containers, where the bulb and roots are clearly visible.

Although a few nutrient formulae that can be made up are presented in Appendix 5, it will probably be easier to use a commercial hydroponic nutrient powder obtainable at horticultural and garden stores.

requirements of the litter will depend on the type of plants being grown. For example, bulbs will require a coarse litter such as wood shavings, whereas seedlings can be transplanted into peat moss or straw.

For large-scale projects, pumps are used to bubble air through the solution; small fish-tank aerators are ideal for anyone wishing to try this method on a small scale. It is also possible to circulate the solution at regular intervals with an electric pump controlled by a time-switch.

Seeds may either be germinated in the litter, which must be kept moist during the germination period, or plants may be started in rockwool cubes and transplanted into the tray. Bulbs, corms and tubers may also be planted directly into the litter.

The solution level must be adjusted from time to time, either by draining solution from the tank if it is too high, or by adding more water if the solution has become too concentrated. The concentration of the nutrient solution can be checked with a *conductivity meter.*

The solution acidity (pH) must be checked from time to time and adjusted if necessary. A brief explanation of pH and conductivity is given on page 36.

The nutrient solution should be replaced once every 7–14 days.

The home gardener may raise crops on a small scale using this method, but it is not generally used commercially as it is somewhat cumbersome. However, the modern version, known as Nutrient Film Technique (NFT), and a modification of this, called Gravel Flow Technique (GFT), are indeed being used effectively on a commercial scale (see page 21).

THE HOME UNIT

For experimentation on a small scale there are several attractive devices.

An ordinary fruit jar can serve as a tank or nutrient container. Fit this with a large cork or a 6 mm (¼ in) thick wooden cover painted with bitumen paint, obtainable from hardware stores. Bore two holes in the

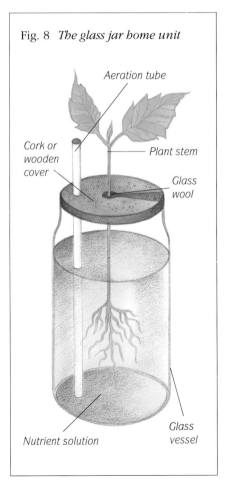

Fig. 8 *The glass jar home unit*

Aeration tube

Cork or wooden cover

Plant stem

Glass wool

Glass vessel

Nutrient solution

NUTRIENT FILM TECHNIQUE (NFT)

NFT is a water culture method of growing crops in a *film* of nutrient liquid. In practice, these films are no more than 1–2 mm (⅛ in) deep, ensuring maximum oxygenation of the roots of the crops. It is not advisable to try NFT for the first time on anything but a small scale.

An early form of NFT was the polythene 'layflat'. Lengths of polythene were laid in parallel rows on the ground, on a slope of 1 in 100. The sides were folded over and clipped in the middle to form a gully through which a film of nutrient solution could flow continuously. The plants were inserted into the 'layflat' through holes cut at suitable intervals.

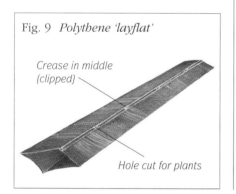

Fig. 9 *Polythene 'layflat'*

Crease in middle (clipped)

Hole cut for plants

Below is a list of the advantages and disadvantages of NFT.

Advantages

• relatively low capital cost
• relative ease of establishing an installation
• because the solution is flowing, it can be of a lower concentration than that needed for a static solution
• no drying out of growing medium between irrigations
• an often rapid turnaround of crops
• optimal root temperatures easily maintained

Disadvantages

• rapid changes of nutrient composition in the 1–2 mm (⅛ in) film of liquid necessitate closer control of nutrient balance compared with other systems
• maintenance of an adequate oxygen supply to the roots when they proliferate presents major problems
• continuous pumping is imperative, and electrical energy is therefore always required
• growing technique is more difficult than that of other hydroponic methods

Basic requirements

Plastic gullies, similar to 'layflats' but more triangular in shape, and with a base at least 150 mm (6 in) wide, are used. They are fastened at the apex with clips or staples. Holes in which the plants will be inserted are left at suitable intervals. The gullies are laid on a slope of about 1 in 100 in parallel rows on a sheet of polythene. A catchment tank is then constructed at the lower part of the slope and a header tank at the upper part. Both of these are set at right angles to the gullies.

Nutrient liquid flows continuously, by gravity, from the header tank, through the gully, down the slope, and into the catchment tank at a rate of 5–10 litres (1–2 gallons) per hour. An electric pump conveys the liquid back into the header tank.

Peat pots are useful for starting seedlings in the NFT system

There is no particular growing medium. Seeds can be planted in small cubes of rockwool, polyurethane foam, or peat ('Jiffy') pots placed in the flowing liquid. The plants' roots grow in the nutrient film itself, which provides water, nutrient and oxygen. During growth the plant forms an extensive root mat on the bottom of the gully. This serves the dual purpose of partially supporting the plant and of absorbing food and water.

A staking system of overhead horizontal wires, to which the plants are attached, is essential.

Lettuces grow well using the Nutrient Film Technique

Fig. 10 *The essential features of NFT, showing detail of a plastic gully*

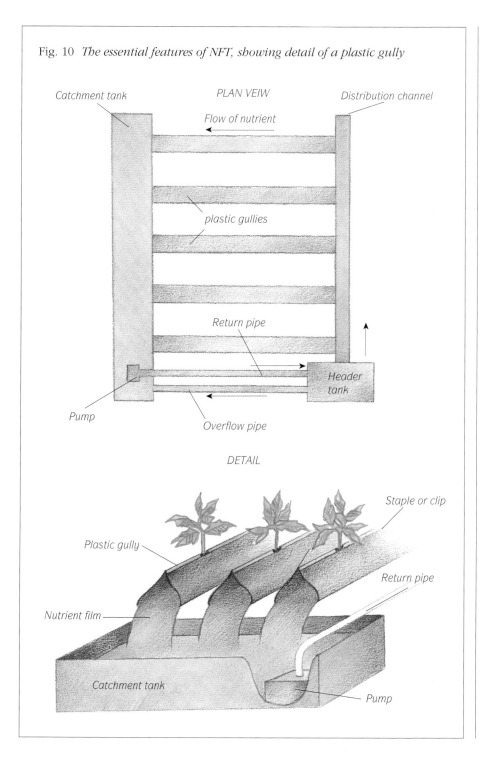

PLAN VEIW

Catchment tank

Distribution channel

Flow of nutrient

plastic gullies

Return pipe

Header tank

Pump

Overflow pipe

DETAIL

Staple or clip

Plastic gully

Return pipe

Nutrient film

Catchment tank

Pump

Seedlings may be sown directly in the gravel

GRAVEL FLOW TECHNIQUE (GFT)

Gravel Flow Technique is a hybrid of NFT and gravel sub-irrigation. Twin plastic gullies are formed from a single roll of black polythene sheet 1–1.5 m (1–1½ yd) wide and 500 microns thick. The sheet is folded in such a way so as to produce two sides 75–100 mm (3–4 in) high. There is a double centre piece of the same height as the sides (see Fig. 11). The width of each gully can also vary from 350 mm to 500 mm (14–20 in).

The gullies, similar to those used in NFT, are laid on the ground with a slope of from 1 to 2 in 100. The sides of the gullies can be supported with metal stakes or wire.

In the UK excellent crops of vegetables and flowers are grown in heated greenhouses using this system. For instance, tomato yields equivalent to 500 tonnes per hectare (220 tons per acre) and 80 cucumbers per plant are commonly grown by the best growers.

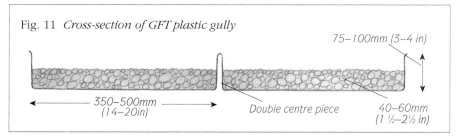

Fig. 11 *Cross-section of GFT plastic gully*

75–100mm (3–4 in)

350–500mm (14–20in)

Double centre piece

40–60mm (1 ½–2½ in)

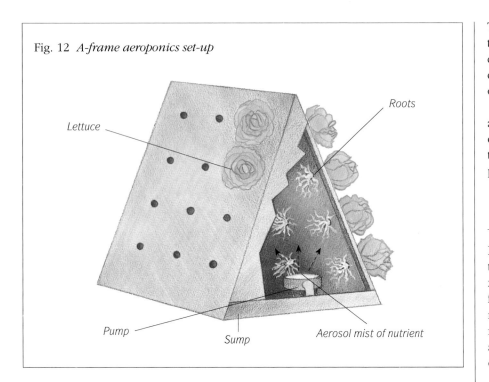

Fig. 12 *A-frame aeroponics set-up*

Lettuce

Roots

Pump

Sump

Aerosol mist of nutrient

The direct planting of seeds and transplanting of seedlings is handled in a similar way to that described in General Construction on page 18.

In some installations heads of lettuce averaging 146 g (5 oz) are picked 76 days after seeding in the polystyrene trays at a plant density of 25 plants per m² (21 plants per sq yd).

AEROPONICS

In this system the plants' roots grow through a support laid either horizontally or in the form of an A-frame. These roots are irrigated at regular intervals with a fine mist of nutrient solution that is physically similar to the sprays produced by domestic aerosol cans.

Popular in Israel, Italy and the United States, this system is on permanent exhibition at 'The Land' section of the Epcot Center, Orlando, Florida. As it is suitable for growing certain vegetables in space, a similar system has been designed by NASA. At Cape Canaveral visitors can see lettuces being grown using this method.

The major differences between GFT and NFT are:

• In GFT a 40–60 mm (1½–2½ in) layer of 6–9 mm (¼–⅜ in) gravel chips is placed in the gulley.
• In GFT the maintenance of an adequate oxygen supply to the roots of the plants is not problematic owing to the 'bubbling' effect of the nutrient solution as it flows through the gravel.
• In GFT larger seeds are sown directly in the gravel; smaller seeds, such as celery, are first germinated in cubes of rockwool or Jiffy pots which are then placed in the gravel bed.
• There are fewer management problems with GFT than with NFT, mainly as a result of the fact that the liquid is agitated as it passes through the gravel chips, resulting in better root aeration.

FLOATING HYDROPONICS

In a water culture system known as *floating hydroponics*, plants grow through 15 mm (½ in) holes in 20 mm (¾ in) thick polystyrene sheets that float on the surface of the nutri-

ent solution. This modified system, which originated in Italy, is used commercially in some countries and is suitable for growing lettuce, strawberries and spinach. It has also been used in public parks in Denmark, where tulips and daffodils have been grown from rafts floating in lakes.

Lettuce in GFT gullies

CHAPTER FOUR

HOME GROWING IN SMALL CONTAINERS

As described in Chapter Three, hydroponic growing can be divided into two broad categories, the first of which has already been covered. The second, which is known as soilless or aggregate culture, is itself sub-divided, according to the method of irrigation used, into:

- *overhead irrigation* in relatively fine media, for example sand, vermiculite and perlite, which is easy to set up, and
- *sub-irrigation* in gravel which, although more costly to install, is technically more efficient.

Tomatoes cultivated in a 'grow bag'

OVERHEAD IRRIGATION

The container

All sorts of containers, including shallow boxes, troughs, drainage channels, bowls or window-boxes may be used for home growing. Materials suitable for these containers are fibre-cement, wood, plastic, earthenware, metal or even glass. A depth of 200–230 mm (8–9 in) allows adequate room for root development, yet is not too deep. It should be remembered that because there is always an ample supply of nutrient available, hydroponic plants generally require less root depth than they would in soil.

The 'grow bag', which is made of polythene and is similar to a 50 kg (110 lb) fertilizer bag sealed at both ends, is popular for home and commercial growing in the UK. The bag is pre-filled with a growing medium such as peat, or a mixture of media.

On one side of the bag three holes, each about 75 mm (3 in) in diameter, are cut at equal distances from one another – one for each of three tomato plants, for example. More holes can easily be cut to accommodate several smaller plants. Irrigation with nutrient solution is carried out from above using a watering-can or by an overhead drip system with 'spaghetti' tubing (see page 68).

TIN CANS are cheap containers but are not recommended because corrosion can be a problem, even when the can is protected by two or three layers of paint.

OTHER CONTAINERS, such as wooden boxes lined with plastic foil, old motor battery cases, guttering, cattle troughs or even old kitchen sinks may be adapted to make containers (see Preparation, page 26). Ensure that the plants have a growing depth of at least 150 mm (6 in).

Painting

It will be necessary to paint the inside surfaces of some of these containers with a coat or two of bitumen paint. If this cannot be obtained, a black acrylic-based paint may be used.

The reasons for this vary, depending on the material. For example, fibre-cement is usually alkaline, which would upset the slightly acid balance of the nutrient solution; wood could rot if not protected; a galvanized metal surface is painted to prevent leaching of the zinc, which is toxic to plants in excess amounts. Unless transparent, plastic will not have to be painted; glass should either be painted or covered with brown paper.

Drainage

Efficient drainage is absolutely essential to growing plants because spaces between the soil 'crumbs' need to be air-filled so that the roots have a good supply of oxygen. If drainage is poor, these spaces become filled with water. This is the aim of ploughing in farming or digging and turning the soil in home gardening. The concept is so important, it is worth repeating: IT IS ESSENTIAL TO ENSURE EFFICIENT DRAINAGE.

This has already been emphasized in Chapter Two, where the importance of oxygen to the roots was mentioned. Lack of aeration is probably the most frequent cause of failure in hydroponic growing.

Growing media

Choosing the growing medium is probably the most important decision to be made when starting out. Compared with the variety of containers at one's disposal, the choice is somewhat limited. Here is a short list of media commonly used with overhead irrigation:

- sand
- vermiculite
- perlite
- rockwool
- cinders
- peat moss
- milled pine-bark
- sawdust
- wood shavings

The first four are all of an inorganic composition but vary somewhat in both physical and chemical properties. The last four are of an organic nature and, being bio-chemical in origin, can vary drastically from source to source. Cinders are somewhere in between. Let us deal briefly with each in turn.

SAND comes in a variety of sizes, shapes, compositions and colours. Technically, any material with particles between 0.25 mm and 2 mm (¹⁄₆₄–¹⁄₈ in) in diameter is classified as sand. Particles may be angular or rounded. Many sands are mixed with fine shell or limestone (calcare-

Sand

Vermiculite

ous sands) or are contaminated with silt or organic matter, which should be washed out of the sand before use, as these tend to clog the system.

Although it is often difficult to obtain, the best sand to use is a clean, coarse river sand with particles 0.6–2 mm (up to ¹⁄₈ in) in diameter. Builders' sand may be used, provided that it is not too fine or too calcareous, which would upset the pH of the nutrient solution. A simple test for determining whether a sand is calcareous or not is to place a 6 mm (¼ in) layer of the sand in a glass tumbler, just cover it with water, and add an equal volume of dilute hydrochloric (not sulphuric) acid. A slight to vigorous effervescence indicates small to large amounts of shell respectively (see also page 46).

NOTE: Hydrochloric acid is obtainable from your local pharmacist. Swimming pool acid consisting of hydrochloric acid may also be used.

VERMICULITE (from Latin *vermis*, meaning 'worm') is a mineral belonging to the mica family, which is mined in several countries. Contrary to popular belief, it has no food value.

Being micaceous in its natural form, vermiculite exists in plates, or lamellae, which are very thin. The bulk of vermiculite mined is used in the building and engineering industries for lightweight concrete and insulation. A small proportion finds use in horticulture.

Before it can be used for any of these purposes, however, it is neces-

sary to change its physical form from the original platelets to an end product consisting of flat air cells. The material that results has the properties of absorbency, lightness (140 kg per m³ [235 lb per cu yd]), poor conductivity of heat (i.e. good insulation) and sterility. The change, known as *exfoliation*, is effected after milling and screening to size, by heating the material to 1,000 °C (1,800 °F) in a furnace. The result is that the hundreds of lamellae are forced outwards into concertina-like particles about twelve times their original thickness.

Exfoliated vermiculite is sold by horticultural stores both for raising seedlings and for general garden use. A finer grade is required for seedlings; particle sizes varying from 2 mm to 4 mm (approximately ¹⁄₈ in) would be suitable. While useful to flat-dwellers and for small-scale growing, vermiculite is not recommended for commercial growers.

Exfoliated vermiculite also has some serious disadvantages. When fresh and full of air-cells it works well, but after an extended period of use the cells break down, reverting to the original flake-like form. Mixed with water these flakes form a pulpy mass similar to porridge, which has just the opposite effect on roots to that intended. The fact that vermiculite is lightweight can be a problem in windy areas, and means that it cannot be mixed with sand. In fact, it should not be mixed with any hard, sharp materials, as they will only assist in the physical breakdown of the vermiculite.

The most serious disadvantage of all is vermiculite's unfavourable pH value. The material available for horticultural use has an alkaline reaction, which is natural for this mineral. The pH value of vermiculite can go as high as 9.5 in water, which is far too high for growing plants. Therefore, when buying vermiculite, it is important to find out the pH value of the batch. If it is above 7.5 it will have to be treated before use. This can be done by soaking it in a dilute solution of mono-ammonium phosphate, which is obtainable from fertilizer companies or horticultural stores. After soaking, wash well with tap water. Recent experience has shown that the high pH of industrial vermiculite is gradually reduced to about 7 by repeated overhead irrigation.

PERLITE, also obtainable from gardening stores, is another mineral that is mined in various countries, including Greece and South Africa. Like vermiculite, it is milled and screened to size, and then treated in a furnace at a temperature of 910 °C (1,670 °F). This creates tiny cavities on a glass-like surface and expands each particle from four to 20 times its original volume. As a result, the crude rock resembles popcorn and has an amazingly low bulk density of 80–110 kg per m³ (135–185 lb per cu yd). The surface area of each particle is greatly increased and the fractured bubbles or cavities tend to absorb water well.

Perlite is a particularly good medium in which to germinate seeds or strike cuttings in hydroponic growing and gives an almost neutral pH value in water.

The only disadvantage is its softness and tendency to turn to powder if not carefully handled.

ROCKWOOL is employed extensively in Europe, particularly in The Netherlands, as a growing medium, though mostly it is used in industry

Perlite

as an insulating material. It is manufactured in factories by heating rock (diabase), limestone and coke together at a high temperature. The resultant molten mass is spun into fine filaments about 5 microns in diameter. Together with certain additives, these are pressed into slabs of various sizes. This can be cut into small cubes in which to plant seeds in an NFT system or it can be used in larger pieces.

Rockwool has a great capacity for absorbing liquids and has a bulk density of around 80 kg per m³ (135 lb per cu yd). Compare this with both vermiculite and perlite.

In The Netherlands there are rockwool installations covering a total area of over 3,500 ha (8,650 acres), for which the overhead drip method of irrigation is used. Large areas of gerbera species are grown, as well as cucumbers, with yields of 100 fruit per m² (83 per sq yd) being commonplace.

CINDERS are the remains of burning coal. Power station ash, which is the fused residue left after burning coal, mixed with a small amount of partially burnt coal, fits this description.

Fresh cinders are usually alkaline in reaction and have to be treated by the grower with dilute sulphuric or phosphoric acid before being used as an aggregate. In some instances, however, this alkalinity has been neutralized by natural weathering in large dumps over several years.

In either case, the lumps have to be broken down and screened – to between 2 mm and 6 mm (⅛ – ¼ in) in diameter.

Cinders

PEAT is not often used by itself as a growing medium but is mixed with other aggregates such as sand or vermiculite. It tends to vary considerably in its properties, depending on its origin. The pH can drop to as low as 4.0, which necessitates the use of limestone to restore neutrality.

Peat

MILLED PINE-BARK is derived from various species of pine and is obtainable from nurseries. The material is milled and screened through a 10 mm (½ in) sieve before use.

Commercial growers use it extensively in nursery bags with the overhead drip method of irrigation.

Milled pine-bark

SAWDUST in its uncomposted form is derived from the same pine species from which the bark was obtained.

This is also used extensively in nursery bags with the overhead drip method of irrigation. Sawdust from other woods may also be used as a growing medium.

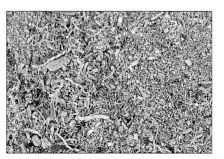

Sawdust

WOOD SHAVINGS from several other species of tree also find use as growing media.

Wood shavings

Preparation of container

For the purpose of illustrating a small-scale hydroponic operation in which an overhead method of irrigation is used, let us consider a fibre-cement window-box of 900 mm x 220 mm x 210 mm (36 in x 8½ in x 8¼ in). Step-by-step instructions for preparation for planting are as follows (see Fig. 13 and Fig. 14):

1. Drill five or six 6 mm (¼ in) holes in the bottom of the window-box; these can either be spaced evenly or zigzagged over its length.

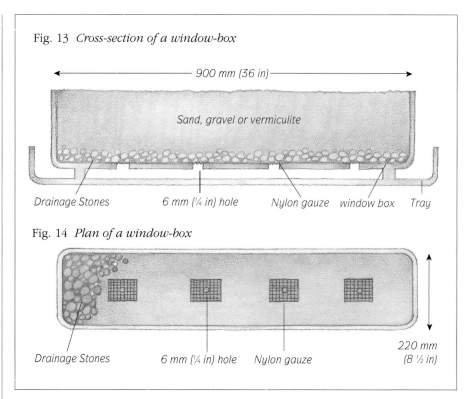

Fig. 13 *Cross-section of a window-box*

900 mm (36 in)

Sand, gravel or vermiculite

Drainage Stones   6 mm (¼ in) hole   Nylon gauze   window box   Tray

Fig. 14 *Plan of a window-box*

Drainage Stones   6 mm (¼ in) hole   Nylon gauze

220 mm (8 ½ in)

2. Unless made from plastic, paint the inside surfaces with bitumen or acrylic-based paint. Make sure that the drainage holes are not blocked up with paint.

3. Cut squares of plastic mesh (preferably nylon, which does not rot) and place these over the holes while the paint is still tacky; or use glue. These squares will act as filters, allowing excess liquid to drain away. Allow the paint to dry completely.

4. To ensure efficient drainage, spread a 25 mm (1 in) layer of stones, broken bricks or earthenware, roughly 6–12 mm (¼–½ in) in diameter, over the bottom of the window-box. Your window-box is now ready to be planted with seeds, cuttings, bulbs or seedlings.

5. Pour in enough of the growing medium you have chosen to fill the box to within about 15 mm (½ in) of the top.

6. Sprinkle *tap water* over the surface of the growing medium, using the fine spray of a garden hose or watering-can, until the whole mass is saturated and water drains *freely* through the holes in the bottom of the container.

7. Let the excess water drain away for a few minutes. Using a small stick, inscribe parallel trenches about 6 mm (¼ in) deep (the depth will depend on the size of the seed; see step 8, below) and 40 mm (1½ in) apart, in the surface of the moist medium.

8. Place the seeds in the trenches at the recommended depth. Very generally speaking, the depth should be about two or three times the diameter of the seed. Very small seeds may be planted individually using a matchstick or fine-haired brush.

9. After sowing the seeds, carefully fill in the trenches with the medium. Sprinkle lightly with water and allow the seed to settle. Do not firm down with the hand.

A multiple planter with several growing pots

Home growing in a small container

NOTE: Very small seeds, such as petunia or celery, may be sown directly after completing step 6. Place the seeds in a pepper pot and sprinkle them over the surface of the moist medium. With a little practice an even spread will result. Now sprinkle a thin layer of *dry* medium over the scattered seeds and lightly water in.

To prepare a tin can for planting, follow the description just given. If, however, you intend using the sub-irrigation method, a series of 3 mm (⅛ in) holes punched in the sides near the bottom of the can will be effective.

Transplanting

SEEDLINGS may be raised in seed-beds or seed-trays in preparation for later transplanting. You may prefer to buy seedlings from an outside source rather than grow your own, though growing one's own seedlings can be great fun.

Whatever your choice, there are usually two possibilities when transplanting:

• transplanting from one type of growing medium into another, or
• transplanting from one medium into the same medium.

The most common example of the first possibility would be transplanting from soil into sand, perlite or vermiculite. In this case, after preparing the container you have chosen for your seedlings as described on page 26, proceed as follows:

1. Remove the seedling from the soil and very gently wash away *as much soil as possible* from the rootlets, being careful not to damage them.

2. Place the whole root system into a suitably sized hole made in the medium into which it is being transplanted. Spacing in the soilless medium should be similar to what it would be in soil. In hydroponics the

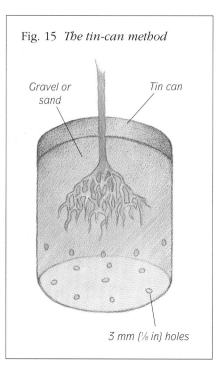

Fig. 15 *The tin-can method*

Gravel or sand

Tin can

3 mm (⅛ in) holes

only real limitation to the number of plants growing in a given area is light, as there is virtually no competition for plant nutrients.

3. Replace the medium around the seedling and gently firm down with the fingers.

Another example of the first possibility would be transplanting from vermiculite into sand or gravel. In this case, you should remove the seedlings carefully using a teaspoon or small kitchen fork, *without* disturbing the clump of vermiculite adhering to the rootlets. Then follow steps 1–3, this page.

An example of the second possibility would be transplanting seedlings from seed-trays containing vermiculite into window-boxes or larger containers also containing vermiculite. The identical procedure is followed, but the danger of wilting is greatly reduced.

BULBS, CORMS AND TUBERS are planted as they would be in soil, with the added advantage that you can plant them closer together and even in a double tier.

CUTTINGS root freely in sand. In fact, carnation cuttings are traditionally rooted in sand using a method that is virtually a hydroponic one.

The plant food

As we know, for hydroponic growing a plant nutrient solution is made to simulate a balanced soil solution. Plant scientists have been able to show from chemical analyses of both plant tissue and soil solutions which elements are needed to provide the nutrient requirements of plants. Naturally, these requirements vary, but, within limits, we know what they are.

Up to this point the preparation of a window-box for soilless cultivation has not differed much from the procedure one would use for growing in soil. The essential difference between the two lies in the method of nutrition. We have only to water a good soil from time to time to produce a crop of tomatoes or a bunch of flowers, but in a soilless medium a complete balanced diet of elements essential to the plant must be provided. This is the *nutrient solution*, sometimes referred to as the *plant nutrients*, the *mineral elements* or, simply, the *plant food*.

Making the nutrient solution

Anyone thinking of starting hydroponics, either as a hobby or perhaps pursuing the more ambitious road of commercial growing, may well be dissuaded by the mistaken perception that hydroponics requires a knowledge of chemistry.

Although chemical knowledge can be useful when making up nutrient solutions, a lack of knowledge need not be a problem, as modern commercial hydroponic nutrient powder is readily available. For readers who wish to make up their own nutrient solutions, several practical formulae are presented in Appendix 5.

The flat-dweller or anyone growing in containers on a small scale, need only buy a small quantity of commercial powder, This will contain the six macro-elements, together with the necessary micro-elements in balanced proportions. The directions on the label will provide all the necessary information.

Generally speaking, the hydroponic powder is dissolved in tap water at the rate of 1 kg per 500 litres (2 lb per 100 gallons). On a smaller scale, this can be achieved by dissolving 10 g (approximately three *level* teaspoons) per 5 litres (1 gallon) water. Both will result in a *full strength* nutrient solution, which is fed to the plants directly. Half-strength solutions are used for seedlings in the early stages.

Do not attempt to use the solution at concentrations greater than full-strength. This is sometimes done in the mistaken belief that the plants will grow more quickly!

A clean 5 litre (1 gallon) plastic container makes a handy storage vessel for the solution. For larger volumes, vessels with a capacity of 20 or 25 litres (4 or 5 gallons) are available. It is important to protect whatever container you are using from light, which tends to cause iron precipitation. Do not use metal containers as these can contaminate the nutrient solution.

Feeding the plants

Having selected the growing medium and the container, and having planted the seeds or transplanted the seedlings of your choice, you can now complete the whole process by irrigating with the already prepared nutrient solution.

This can be carried out using one of three different methods:

- overhead watering
- dry-feeding
- sub-irrigation

The last of these methods is reserved specifically for irrigating gravel and then usually for a larger-scale project, such as a home installation. It will nevertheless be described later in this chapter since it can be successful on a small scale.

Overhead watering

This is about the most straightforward irrigation method we can use in hydroponics. Once made up, the nutrient solution is poured into a watering-can fitted with a fine rose, and sprinkled over the growing medium until it is moist – it should be similar to a wetted sponge that has been wrung out. It does not matter if the foliage is wetted by the nutrient, provided that the nutrient's concentration is not greater than the recommended maximum.

Further details on irrigating sand and vermiculite are given below, but common sense will be a reliable guide. This would tell you, for example, that absorbent types of growing media, such as vermiculite or sawdust, would need less frequent irrigation than the less absorbent sand or perlite.

In general, the plants themselves will be the best guide to the frequency of irrigation. Observe them and respond to their needs.

SAND A fine sand usually needs a daily irrigation in summer – a coarse sand might need two. The frequency of irrigation will be determined by factors such as the humidity, exposure to sun, presence or absence of wind, type of plant being grown (leafy or otherwise), the stage of growth, the size of the container in relation to the size of the plants being grown, the size and shape of the medium (for example, rounded or angular), and so on.

The best gauge is the moisture content of the medium, rather than the nutrient requirement of the plants. As a result, when water is needed the plants will be receiving nutrient as well. It is quite in order, however, to use plain water occasionally – say once a week – especially under hot, drying conditions.

In time you will be guided by experience as to the correct irrigation regime to use when growing hydroponically in sand.

VERMICULITE Owing to its high degree of absorbency, vermiculite requires less frequent irrigation than most other media. After the initial soaking (see step 6 on page 26) it will be necessary to water only every second day in summer while the plants are still young. In winter less frequent irrigation, consistent with sufficient nutrition, can be given.

Allow any excess nutrient solution to run to waste through the drainage holes and do not attempt to collect this for re-use. Water with freshly made nutrient every time.

Dry-feeding

This is a simple, though not necessarily the most effective, way in which hydroponics can be practised. As the name implies, food is given to the plants in the form of a dry powder, rather than in solution. Since the dry plant food has first to be dissolved by the water, this method of irrigation does not provide as even a distribution as the overhead irrigation of a pre-dissolved nutrient would.

For each square metre (square yard) of growing area thinly sprinkle about 25 g (1 oz) of dry nutrient powder around the plants. This is only a rough guide and you may have to increase or decrease this amount; experience will be the best guide. Then simply apply water.

A single application should last between one and two weeks, again depending on several factors, some of which have already been mentioned. It is important not to let the bed dry out. For outdoor plants it may become necessary to apply plant food at twice-weekly intervals to offset that lost by leaching during wet weather.

One disadvantage of this method of feeding is that it is not always easy to apply dry powder as the plants grow bigger. With lettuce, for example, this procedure becomes difficult because of the low-lying leafy nature of the plant.

SUB-IRRIGATION

This is an extremely efficient system that produces outstanding results with a variety of flower and vegetable crops. It requires the nutrient solution to be pumped or forced by gravity through the bed of growing medium from below, almost to its surface, from where it drains back again into the nutrient reservoir. The used solution is topped up with water if necessary and re-used for a period of ten days to two weeks.

Sub-irrigation not only uses less water than the overhead method of application, but also ensures excellent aeration. This is due to the fact that all the old air is displaced during irrigation, to be replaced by the fresh air sucked in from the top during drainage back into the nutrient reservoir.

Gravel or coarse sand are ideal aggregates and are used mostly in commercial installations and for home growing in hydroponic beds. But as we are concerned here with small-scale growing, let us consider the possibilities.

Setting up window-boxes and larger containers for sub-irrigation

1. You will need a watertight growing trough, preferably made of plastic and about 200 mm (8 in) deep. At one end, fit this container with a small inlet pipe, 12 mm (½ in) in diameter, through a small hole positioned near the bottom.

2. Attach a short length of plastic or rubber hose to this. This length of hose fits over a similar pipe, which is fixed to the bottom of a bucket or 20 litre (4 gallon) plastic reservoir. The size of the reservoir will be limited by the ability of the grower to

lift weights! A 20 litre (4 gallon) container filled with nutrient solution weighs approximately 20 kg (44 lb), which seems to be the convenient upper limit for hand operation. A light block and tackle could be rigged to the reservoir for lifting larger volumes.

3. Fill the trough with gravel about 3 mm (⅛ in) in diameter. Each square metre of this medium will require about 100 litres of nutrient solution for complete irrigation (20 gallons per sq yd). For hand operation, this will limit the grower to about 0.2 m² (¼ sq yd), an area slightly larger than a small window-box.

Using an electric pump connected to the reservoir, you can irrigate a growing area of almost unlimited size. With the additional use of a time-clock the whole operation can be automated.

4. So as not to disturb the gravel during irrigation, place a length of half-round plastic piping, made by cutting along the diameter of a 75 mm (3 in) PVC pipe, over the inlet pipe, along the length of the trough.

5. Drill 3 mm (⅛ in) holes close together in a zigzag pattern along the length of this pipe. In order to prevent any fine material finding its way into the pipe, wrap plastic gauze around it. Alternatively, place a shallow layer of stones that are larger than the gravel particles, around the pipe.

Irrigation

In summer, daily irrigation is recommended. Occasional watering from above with fresh tap water is also good growing practice.

With manual irrigation, the nutrient solution is forced into the trough by raising the reservoir (see Fig. 16). If you have an electric pump, simply switch it on. Solution will flow into the gravel in both cases. When the level of the liquid is about 25 mm (1 in) from the surface of the gravel, lower the reservoir or switch off the pump. All excess liquid will flow back into the reservoir where it can be topped up with water occasionally. The same nutrient can be used repeatedly for seven to ten days.

The frequency of irrigation will

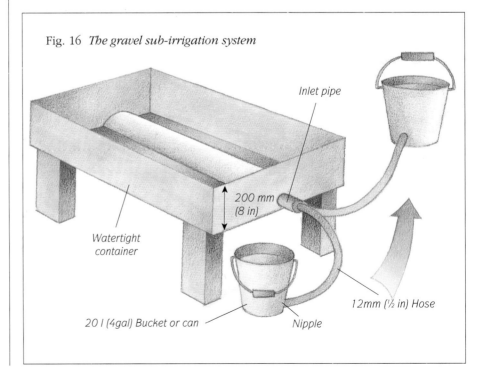

Fig. 16 *The gravel sub-irrigation system*

Inlet pipe

200 mm (8 in)

Watertight container

20 l (4gal) Bucket or can

12mm (½ in) Hose

Nipple

depend on factors such as the size and type of the plants being grown, the prevailing climatic conditions, and others. Leafy plants like lettuce would require more frequent irrigation than gladioli, for example. Hot, windy conditions also make more than one irrigation necessary. So, although a single daily irrigation has been recommended, one may need to water twice or three times daily. Experience will be the best guide.

One modification of this basic design, devised in The Netherlands, is illustrated in Fig. 17. In this system the liquid nutrient is pumped into one end of the bed. From here it flows through the gravel at a height determined by an adjustable overflow. There is no central pipe or channel at the bottom of the bed.

During the irrigation cycle the solution returns to the reservoir through the overflow tube, thus entraining oxygen. After a while fully aerated solution flows through the gravel bed. The irrigation cycle is complete after total replacement of the old by the new, aerated, solution. Pumping time will depend on the length of the bed. After the pump has been switched off manually or mechanically all the liquid will finally drain back into the reservoir through the escape orifice.

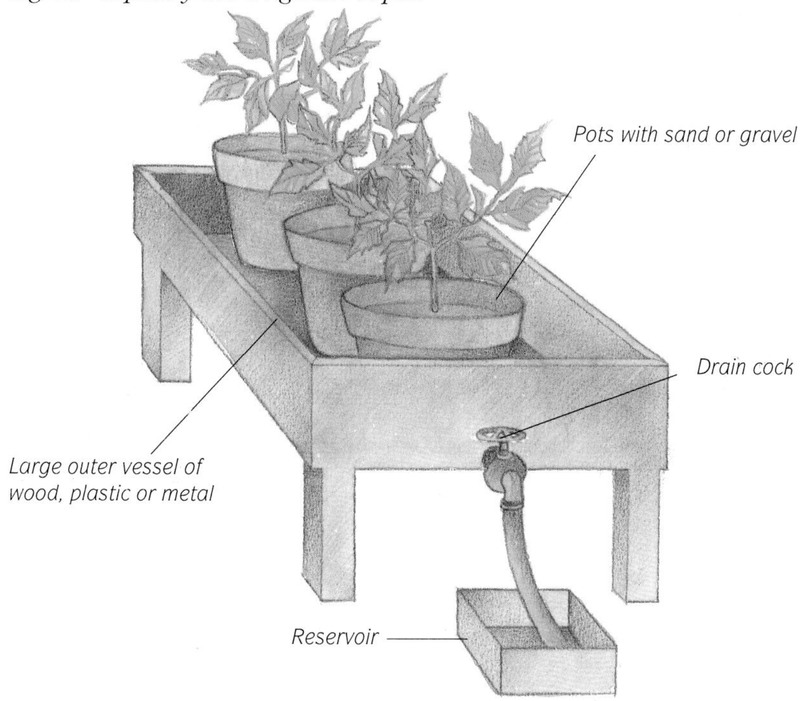

Setting up pots and other small containers

Many nurseries use what might be called *capillary sub-irrigation* for watering their seedlings in pots.

Fig. 17. *Modified gravel sub-irrigation system*

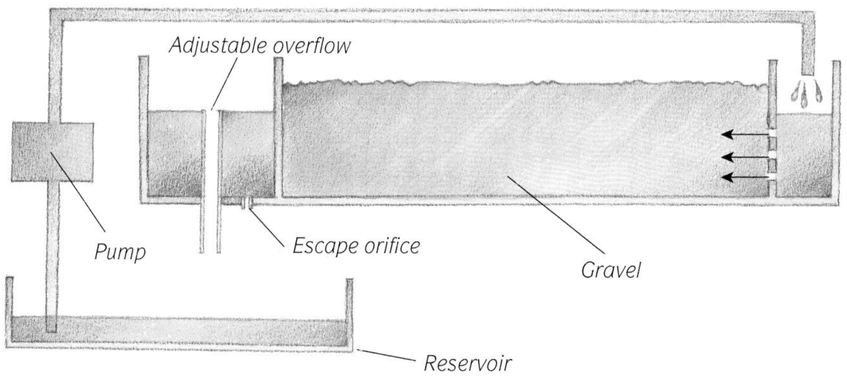

Adjustable overflow

Pump

Escape orifice

Gravel

Reservoir

Fig. 18 *Capillary sub-irrigation in pots*

Pots with sand or gravel

Drain cock

Large outer vessel of wood, plastic or metal

Reservoir

These plastic pots are ideal for capillary sub-irrigation

The pots with plants growing in them are placed in a shallow trough that is about 100 mm (4 in) deep and fitted with an external tap, if possible. Nutrient solution or water is poured into the trough so as to submerge at least one-third of the pot. This needs very careful levelling to avoid floods! After 20–30 minutes liquid will rise up into the pot through the drainage holes at the bottom. When the growing medium is sufficiently moistened, the liquid is drained or siphoned away into the nutrient reservoir. A very useful additional item in this setup would be a fibreglass mat in the bottom of the tray; this holds some solution and decreases the need for frequent sub-irrigation.

This system is only suitable for relatively fine growing media, such as sand or perlite (see Fig. 18).

TUBE CULTURE

Finally, brief mention must be made of the tube culture system, if only because of its ingenuity and the fact that it is easy to set up.

Fig. 19 illustrates the main features of this system.

Lettuce grown by tube culture method

Basically, the unit is constructed from two PVC tubes of the same length but different diameters. The lower tube, 100 mm (4 in) in diameter and sealed at both ends, is the nutrient reservoir. The upper tube, 150 mm (6 in) in diameter, is cut longitudinally at about 80 per cent of its diameter (see Fig. 19). About 120 mm (4¾ in) deep, this serves as the growing trough, and is filled with a growing medium to within 10 mm (½ in) of the top. The two are held together on a stand or with clamps, and connected with PVC tubes as shown. A small air-pump, such as a fish tank aerator, connects to the top of the lower tube. When the air-pump is activated a pressure builds up in the nutrient trough, forcing nutrient into the upper trough through the connecting tube. A time-clock may be fitted to the aerator if desired.

A growing medium of perlite is particularly suitable for this method.

MISCELLANEOUS MANAGEMENT NOTES

There are many queries that may occur to the reader after setting up the hydroponic installation. Some of these, such as taste and nutritional value of hydroponic vegetables, yields compared with soil, and so on, will be dealt with in a later chapter. But there are others of a more practical nature that you should know something about. For example:

- light requirements
- rain
- wilting
- flushing with water
- growth of algae
- staking plants
- wind
- water quality

These factors are discussed below.

Light requirements

One of the most important factors that determines the success of growing plants is the quantity and intensity of light falling on the leaves. After all, this energy powers the biochemical factory in the plants.

Based on their energy requirements, plants may be roughly divided into three classes. Two examples of *high energy* plants are the tomato and the cucumber; many indoor ornamentals (*Ficus* and most ferns) are good examples of *low energy* plants. In the middle class are the *medium energy* plants, such as celery and begonia.

Unless adequate light is available, it is no good trying to raise tomatoes, for example, indoors. Growing plants near windows is not a good solution as this causes them to grow out tall towards the light and become spindly and weak. Instead, try a verandah or an area next to a wall outside, where the plant will receive adequate sunlight.

From this we learn that the very first rule is to find a situation suited to the plant being grown.

Rain

Large raindrops falling on vermiculite or other fragile media will tend to disturb the surface, and may even uproot seedlings. However, unless prolonged and torrential, rain will generally do no harm. If the installation is in a rainy area, it may be necessary to arrange for some type of shelter, such as a greenhouse, cloche or 'tunnel'.

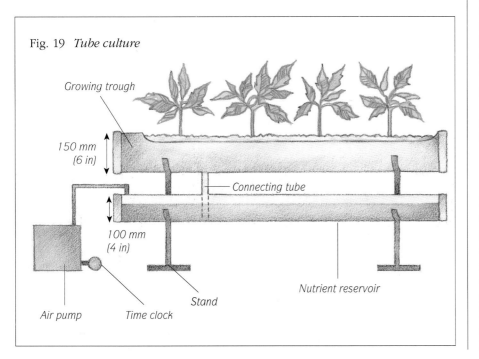

Fig. 19 *Tube culture*

Growing trough

150 mm (6 in)

Connecting tube

100 mm (4 in)

Nutrient reservoir

Air pump

Time clock

Stand

A cloche provides ideal shelter for low-lying crops

Wilting

Temporary wilting is usually a sign of insufficient moisture in the growing medium. This often occurs during the hottest part of the day when transpiration (see page 13) is most rapid. To remedy this, add water or dilute nutrient solution to the medium as soon as possible.

Repeated daily wilting in hot weather could suggest that the plants are being grown in too small a container. This can be solved by transplanting them into a larger pot.

Certain fungal and bacterial diseases can also cause wilting in some plants. (See Chapter Ten, which deals with diseases more thoroughly.)

Flushing with water

It is good practice to occasionally wash out any salts accumulated in the growing medium. Flush the medium with tap water once every six weeks. Commence normal feeding the next day.

Growth of algae

If the growing medium has been kept too moist, a green scum known as algae will sometimes appear on its surface. These are forms of life that grow on nutrified media in the presence of light. Apart from their objectionable appearance and the fact that to a small degree they are competing with the plants for nutrients, no real harm will be done.

One way of preventing the growth of algae is to cut out the light by placing 12 mm (½ in) stones over the surface of the medium. On a small scale, in hyacinth glasses for example, a small piece of charcoal will inhibit algae growth.

Staking plants

Staking plants presents a problem for small-scale growers. Clearly, it is not practicable to use a wooden stake in a soft material such as vermiculite, though it is possible in sand or gravel. An alternative is to rig up an external system using overhead wires. This is the practice in commercial growing, for plants such as tomatoes and cucumbers.

Wind

Staking is essential in windy areas. Without stakes it would not be possible to grow anything but short or low-lying plants. The use of windbreaks is one partial solution to this problem. In commercial practice in some countries shadecloth is used for this purpose.

Water quality

This will be considered in more detail in the next chapter. Suffice it to say that tap water in most parts of the world will be suitable for hydroponic use. Very brackish waters or extremely hard waters should be avoided. If no other source is available, collected rainwater is an excellent alternative.

CHAPTER FIVE
PREPARING NUTRIENT SOLUTIONS

The nutrient solution or liquid plant food used in hydroponics consists of a mixture of fertilizer-grade salts dissolved in water.

In this chapter we shall discuss the various options that are available to the reader for making the nutrient solution; there is also a brief review of water quality and an introduction to the important concepts of pH and conductivity.

Some fertilizer salts – potassium chloride, for example – provide the plant with a single element, in this case, potassium. Only traces of the chloride part of the salt are utilized by the plant. Other salts, like ammonium phosphate, supply both nitrogen and phosphorus. In a similar manner, all nutrient elements are derived from one or other salt. The role played by these elements has already been briefly alluded to (see page 17).

Appendix 3 contains a list of the main fertilizer salts that provide the macro-elements used in compounding nutrient formulae. All the salts for the micro-elements are listed in Appendix 4.

There are two ways in which the nutrient mixtures required for hydroponic growing can be provided:

• The grower may use one of the formulae given in Appendix 5 (or found in other books and publications on this subject) and make his or her own, or
• the grower may prefer to purchase a commercially mixed nutrient powder obtainable from garden stores and some supermarkets.

A third possiblility exists for those growers with the necessary technical background, who may prefer to formulate their own mixtures.

Let us discuss the first two options in greater detail.

USING A PUBLISHED FORMULA

In order to make up a mixture according to one of the formulae in Appendix 5 (or a formula taken from another book), the grower will have to weigh out the four or five salts supplying the macro-elements, plus some six different salts for the micro-elements. Here one has the choice of weighing and mixing at home, or obtaining the services of a pharmacist or laboratory.

The reader will notice that relatively small amounts of chemicals are required for the micro-element formula in Appendix 4. Although the chemical balance would be ideal for weighing out these small amounts, either photographers' scales or those used for weighing letters would also be effective.

The weighing of salts for the macro-elements should present less of a problem. A good-quality kitchen scale which is accurate to the nearest 20 grams (ounce), will be satisfactory.

Buying chemicals

Before weighing out each chemical, the grower will have to purchase the various salts listed in the chosen formula. Undoubtedly, the cheapest source is the fertilizer-grade chemical obtainable from the fertilizer manufacturer. Unfortunately, these are usually sold in 50 kg (110 lb) bags, which may suit people growing in hydroponic beds, but would be far too much for the small-scale grower wishing to make up limited quantities of powder. However, some garden stores do sell smaller quantities of this grade.

Small quantities of chemicals are obtainable from pharmacies, but these are of the very pure B.P.-grade, and are relatively expensive.

Industrial chemical supply companies usually stock the industrial- or food-grade chemicals, which are priced between the fertilizer- and B.P.- grade. The disadvantage for the small-scale grower is that these are usually also packed in 25 kg (55 lb) or 50 kg (110 lb) bags.

Mixing

After weighing out the separate chemicals it is best to add each to at least 75 per cent of the total amount of water to be used. For example, if 100 litres (22 gallons) of nutrient solution is being prepared, at least 75 litres (16½ gallons) of water should be present in the mixing container before the addition of any salts. It is also good practice to add the calcium salts last of all. Some calcium salts include the superphosphates – both normal and triple – which leave a small insoluble sediment after solution in water. This can be ignored.

Never attempt to make the nutrient solution more concentrated than the formula calls for, as this will cause precipitation of insoluble salts of calcium and magnesium.

Micro-elements

The addition of the micro-elements or trace elements probably presents the greatest problem in mixing for the home grower. Perhaps the easiest way to approach this is to make a single mixture of the six trace elements, the so-called *trace element mixture (TEM)* listed in Appendix 4. This product is then added to the mixture of macro-elements as a dry powder (let us call this the *trace element dry mix* or *TEDM*) in the amount specified in the given formula.

Alternatively, the 100 g (3½ oz) referrred to in Appendix 4 may be dissolved in 5 litres (1 gallon) of water, to which is added about 1 ml (15 drops) of concentrated sulphuric acid (call this *trace element concentrate* or *TEC*). This will be sufficient for fifty additions of TEC, each of 100 ml (3½ fl oz), to every 100 litres (22 gallons) of nutrient solution made up according to Appendix 5. Store the TEC in a dark container.

USING A COMMERCIAL NUTRIENT POWDER

The pre-mixed commercial hydroponic nutrient powder is obtainable from garden stores and some supermarkets. It contains all the necessary macro- and micro-elements in proportions suitable for growing most plants. All that is necessary is to follow the mixing instructions that are printed on the label. Usually, the requirement is to dissolve one part, by weight, of the powder in 500 parts, by volume, of water. This is the same as dissolving 10 g (about 3 level teaspoons) of powder in 5 litres (1 gallon) of water.

WATER QUALITY

Agriculture, of which hydroponics is a branch, requires water of suitable quality. Very generally speaking, any water that is potable, or fit for drinking, would be considered suitable for agricultural purposes.

Commercial nutrient powder with equipment for preparing and testing nutrient solutions

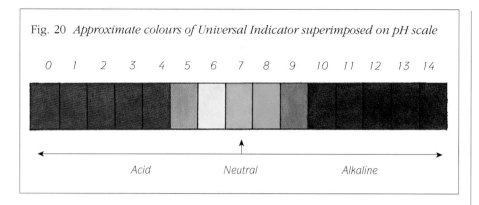

Fig. 20 *Approximate colours of Universal Indicator superimposed on pH scale*

0 1 2 3 4 5 6 7 8 9 10 11 12 13 14

Acid   Neutral   Alkaline

All water contains dissolved solids and gases. Sea water, which usually cannot be used for growing land plants, contains 3.5 per cent dissolved salts, of which common salt (sodium chloride) makes up two-thirds. There are procedures for removing these salts but they are usually expensive and often uneconomical, especially on a small scale. In the Persian Gulf region, Saudi Arabia distills sea water to produce almost pure water for its inhabitants. Other methods include deionization and reverse osmosis. These procedures are viable only on a relatively large scale.

Any prospective commercial grower would need to have a chemical analysis done of the water he or she proposes to use, for the following:

• total dissolved solids (TDS)
• chlorides (if TDS exceed 500 mg/litre [35 grains/gallon])
• alkalinity
• pH value
• heavy metals, sulphides and 'free' chlorine, if suspected

The home grower will only need an analysis if taste shows the water to be brackish.

WHAT IS pH VALUE?

No one writing about hydroponics can avoid mentioning the term 'pH' (note the small 'p' and capital 'H').

This is simply a measure of the acidity or alkalinity of a solution, which is indicated by a number on a scale from 0 to 14. Pure water, which is neutral, has a pH of 7, acid solutions have a pH lower than 7, and alkaline soltions a pH greater than 7. Fig. 20 illustrates this in diagrammatic form.

Since an elementary knowledge of chemistry would be required to thoroughly understand these concepts, we will not attempt a detailed explanation. Suffice it to say, however, that each type of plant grows best within a specific pH range. While the vast majority of plants prefer the slightly acidic range of pH 6.0–6.5, the so-called acid-loving plants, for example, the azalea, the hydrangea and the protea, do best at pH 4–5. Still others, the lime-loving plants, like the sweet pea and the stock, like a pH of 6.5–8. The general recommendation for growers is to *aim for a pH of 6.0*. Most commercial nutrient formulations should produce a pH close to this when dissolved in tap water.

It must also be pointed out that during the one or two weeks' life of the nutrient solution, its pH value is likely to change, usually in an alkaline direction. This is due to the differential uptake by the plants of the different parts of the salts dissolved in the water.

Two obvious questions are likely to arise: firstly, 'How do I determine pH value?', and secondly, 'How do I alter pH?'. Both these questions are

of great importance but detailed explanations are beyond the scope of this book. Only brief mention of pH and conductivity is made below. For a full discussion, consult a more advanced book on the subject, such as *Hydroponics: The Complete Guide to Gardening Without Soil* by Dudley Harris (New Holland Publishers, London, 1994).

How to determine pH

One can use any of the following methods for assessing pH values:

• universal indicator paper
• universal indicator solution
• electric pH meter

These are obtainable from laboratory suppliers (see also Appendix 2).

How to alter pH

To make an alkaline solution more acidic (i.e. to lower the pH) add – in small quantities at a time – *dilute sulphuric acid* to the nutrient solution. To raise the pH, add a slurry of *builders' lime* to the nutrient solution. Trial and error will finally produce the desired result.

ELECTRICAL CONDUCTIVITY (EC)

A conductivity (or EC) meter is used to determine the approximate amount of dissolved solids in solution. Again, this can be ignored if one is growing on a small scale in pots and window-boxes, but it is recommended that larger-scale hydroponic growers make regular conductivity measurements.

The basic unit of measurement is the *siemens* (S) and the general range in which to grow plants is 1,500–2,500 microsiemens (µS) or 1.5–2.5 millisiemens (mS).

Tap waters in most areas will have acceptably low conductivities for use as make-up waters.

CHAPTER SIX

INDOOR ORNAMENTAL PLANTS

Most people seem to enjoy the greenery provided by indoor plants. Perhaps this is a result of living in flats and houses, particularly in the urban areas, where we have been virtually cut off from Nature. The urge to grow indoor plants is a way of counteracting this isolation.

There are two excellent hydroponic methods for growing ornamentals in the home – namely *hydroculture* and the *wick system.*

The variety of indoor plants that can be grown by either of these hydroponic methods is numerous. Here is a short list of examples:

Aglaonema	*Hedera*
Anthurium	*Maranta*
Aphelandra	*Monstera*
Asparagus (fern)	(Delicious
Begonia	Monster)
Bromeliads	*Peperomia*
Cacti	*Philodendron*
Chlorophytum	*Saintpaulia*
Coleus	(African
Cyclamen	violet)
Dieffenbachia	*Sansevieria*
Dracaena	*Schefflera*
Ficus	*Yucca*

HYDROCULTURE

Developed in Europe where it is still extensively practised today, hydroculture is eminently suitable for growing indoor plants, even small trees, in a medium of specially prepared clay pellets. This system is not, however, suitable for outdoor growing, nor, generally, for growing vegetables. The name given to these pellets is *leca*, which is an acronym for the words 'light expanded clay

Ornamental plants will enhance any patio

aggregate'. These pellets are made of clay that has been heat treated in a furnace at 1,200 °C (2,000 °F). The pellets are about the size of marbles (8–16 mm [¼ – ½ in]) but can also be obtained in smaller diameters of 2–8 mm (⅛ – ¼ in).

The advantage of using leca is that just the correct amount of water is supplied to the plants' roots by capillary action between the clay particles. At the same time, the ample air spaces provide all the oxygen required by the roots (see Fig. 21).

Peperomia species in leca

Most commonly, two containers are used for hydroculture growing – the outer container, which is the *reservoir* for one or more inner containers or *growing pots*. The outer container is watertight but the growing pots have holes or slits in them around the bottom, thus allowing access to liquid nutrient in the reservoir. The plants grow in the pots, which are appropriate to the size of the plant. Individual containers, as well as attractive multiple planters containing more than one pot, are obtainable from firms specializing in hydroculture growing.

The other two essential parts of the system are the nutrient height *indicator* and the nutrient *filling tube,* usually combined into a single tube. Initially, the growing pot, containing a plant that has its roots buried in leca pellets, is placed in the outer reservoir with the top of the pot at the same level as the top of the reservoir. A combined indicator and filling tube is arranged at one side of the reservoir so that the bottom of this tube, when the indicator reads 'minimum', is flush with the bottom of the growing pot. Leca is now placed in the reservoir, securing the growing pot in position. For recently transplanted plants, plain water is

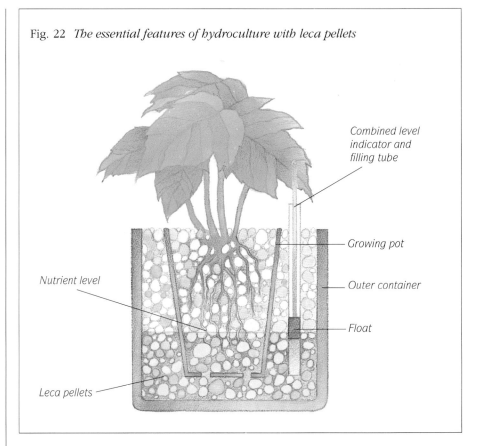

Fig. 22 *The essential features of hydroculture with leca pellets*

Combined level indicator and filling tube

Growing pot

Outer container

Nutrient level

Float

Leca pellets

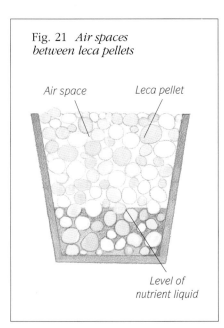

Fig. 21 *Air spaces between leca pellets*

Air space

Leca pellet

Level of nutrient liquid

poured through the filling tube until the indicator shows 'maximum'. Ideally, the level of the liquid should be about one-third of the depth of the leca in the pot at this point. The salient features of a hydroculture set-up are shown in Fig. 22.

Single pot containers can also be used. These are a combination of the reservoir and growing pot in one vessel and therefore will not have drainage holes. A similar indicator/filling tube arrangement is placed in the leca towards the side of the pot.

Conversion from soil to leca

1. Wash the soil carefully but thoroughly from the plants' roots.

2. Place the leca in a basin and rinse with water.

3. Place the washed leca in the growing container or pot, to a height of about a quarter of its depth.

4. Carefully place the plant in the pot and fill with leca, to within about 12 mm (½ in) from the top.

5. Place the pot or pots into the outer container and fill with leca if the system is designed for this.

6. Add water until the indicator reads 'maximum'.

As the roots absorb water, the water level indicator will fall. When the indicator is close to 'minimum', replenish with nutrient solution until the reading is restored to 'maximum'. Apart from this, very little other maintainance is required.

After a few weeks the new plants will develop special fleshy, white 'water' roots as they adapt to the new medium.

Try to grow the plants you have converted to hydroculture under the same conditions in which you would have grown them in soil. In other

Remove the plant from its pot

Shake off as much soil as possible

Wash off the remainder of the soil

Wash the leca pellets before use

Place the plant in the pot and fill with washed leca

words, the same attention must be given to the plants' light requirements and humidity, absence of draughts and general care. Any good book on indoor plants should have all the necessary information. The rewards that await the grower of ornamentals by hydroculture are really worth the trouble taken to make the conversion from soil.

Some commercial firms provide plants already established in leca. These are also sold to large companies for beautifying the office environment. Plants grown by hydroculture are to be found decorating offices and homes all over Europe, the United Kingdom, Scandinavia and the Americas.

THE WICK SYSTEM

In this system, a wick, usually made of braided nylon, is used to water the plants. This is based on the principle that water rises in capillary spaces.

One of the main advantages of this system is the elimination of manual watering for relatively long periods of time. Instead, a reservoir has only to be topped up at intervals – which could be as long as three months – depending on its capacity. An added advantage is that capillary watering ensures a stable and optimum moisture content in the growing medium. This effectively discourages diseases brought about by overwatering.

This self-watering technique makes it possible for the home- or flat-dweller to enhance the beauty of the environment with an absolute minimum of labour. Imagine taking a vacation without having to arrange for someone to water your plants while you are away!

Step-by-step instructions for setting up

The basic requirements are:

- a plastic pot
- a suitable wick, made of braided nylon cord (see step 2 on page 41)
- a growing medium, ideally perlite; vermiculite and some of the other finer media may be used if perlite is not available. However, perlite has the unique property of retaining an optimum water content when watered by a wick.
- a reservoir for the nutrient solution
- a hydroponic nutrient powder

1. Drill a hole through the middle of the base of a suitably sized plastic pot (say, 180 mm [7 in] high, and 150 mm [6 in] in diameter). The hole should be large enough to accommodate the wick enclosed in a collar of plastic made from a short length of polythene tube (see Fig. 23).

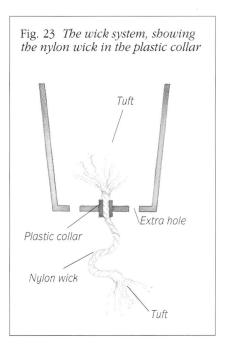

Fig. 23 *The wick system, showing the nylon wick in the plastic collar*

Tuft

Extra hole

Plastic collar

Nylon wick

Tuft

The exotic Yucca *does well in leca*

Apart from the central hole, there should be at least one hole in the bottom of the pot. All additional holes, other than the central one accommodating the wick, should be covered with a piece of nylon gauze.

Insert the braided nylon cord in a plastic tube collar

2. Cut a 250 mm (10 in) length of 6–9 mm (¼–⅜ in) braided nylon cord. The length will depend on the depth of the reservoir and the height of the pot, but the cord should be long enough to reach from the bottom of the reservoir to a depth of about one-third into the pot (see Fig. 24).

Untwine the fibres at each end of the cord

3. Insert the wick through the collar and fit it snugly into the central hole in the bottom of the pot. Tease out or unwind the fibres to make a tuft at each end of the wick.

4. Place perlite (1–3 mm [⅛ in] size) in the pot to within 10 mm (½ in) of the top. Saturate with water and allow the excess to drain away.

Fill the pot with perlite and place over a reservoir

5. Fill a suitable opaque plastic reservoir with water and add about 1 g (¼ tsp) hydroponic nutrient powder per litre (2 pints).

It is useful, though not essential, to have a floating marker to indicate the level of the liquid in the reservoir. You can make this by attaching a small cube of foam plastic to a drink-

ing straw and floating this in the liquid through a hole in the cover. Your wick system is now set up and ready for use.

6. After carefully washing the soil from the roots (see Conversion from soil to leca, page 38), transplant your indoor plant into the perlite, gently firming down by hand. The only task remaining is to replenish the nutrient solution when the reservoir is almost dry.

Several pots with wicks may be set up over a window-box reservoir. The reservoir must be bituminized inside if necessary (see page 18) and fitted with a suitable cover that has holes in it to allow the wicks to pass through. This arrangement can be painted on the outside and attractively displayed in wooden or wrought-iron stands.

Whether growing in leca or using the wick system, give your plants the attention they deserve, and although indoor plants are generally healthy, be on the look-out for any sign of pests or diseases. These should be handled in the same way as if the plants were growing in soil.

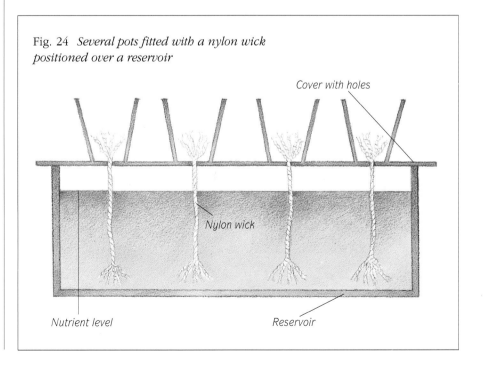

Fig. 24 *Several pots fitted with a nylon wick positioned over a reservoir*

Cover with holes

Nylon wick

Nutrient level

Reservoir

CHAPTER SEVEN

HOME GROWING IN HYDROPONIC BEDS

In an outdoor hydroponic installation the home-grower will be able to produce year-round supplies of quality vegetables and flowers for the family – and all this in an absolute minimum of space! As little as 15 m² (18 sq yd) is sufficient to produce 120 kg (265 lb) of tomatoes, as well as 150 cucumbers and 150 beetroot, plus lettuce, radish and peppers, which can be picked fresh when required.

For hydroponic growing on this scale one has a choice of two systems, which have already been mentioned in an earlier chapter. They are the *dry-feed* system (see page 29) and *sub-irrigation in gravel* (see page 30). The first is by far the easier and less expensive to set up, differing little from conventional growing in soil. Sub-irrigation in gravel, on the other hand, while probably the most effective method of raising crops, is more difficult to set up. It is, however, well suited to automation and should commend itself to anyone fascinated by gadgets.

DRY-FEEDING

To construct a 15 m² (18 sq yd) dry-feed bed, follow these simple, step-by-step instructions:

1. In a section of your garden that receives adequate sunlight, dig an area about 1.25 m (4 ft) wide and 12 m (38 ft) long (there is virtually no limit to width or length) and about 350 mm (14 in) deep. Arrange a north-south orientation if possible.

Check the drainage properties of the soil in the bottom of the excavated area by soaking it thoroughly with water and observing how long it takes the excess to drain away. If you find that the soil is impervious to water it may be necessary to lay drainage channels in the bottom. Under most circumstances, however, the water will eventually seep into the sub-soil.

2. Line the excavated area with sheets of suitable material to separate it from the soil. Wood, cement sections, galvanized iron or loosely packed bricks would all be suitable.

Wood must be protected with bitumen or an acrylic paint.

3. If using wood, cut pieces at least 12 mm (½ in) thick and 300 mm (12 in) wide, making sure that you have enough to line the length and width of the dug-out area. Place these in the excavation; they should protrude about 25 mm (1 in) above ground level (see Fig. 25 and Fig. 26).

If using a material such as wood, it might be necessary to provide additional lateral support. To do this, knock sections of metal piping or wooden stakes into the ground at suitable intervals. Should any extra support be required, wooden cross-braces can be nailed across the sides.

4. For drainage purposes, place a 120 mm (5 in) layer of stones, at least 38 mm (1½ in) in diameter, into the bottom of the excavation. Pieces of broken brick or rubble may be substituted. On top of the drainage

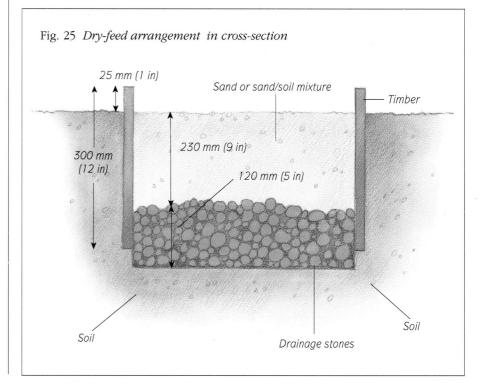

Fig. 25 *Dry-feed arrangement in cross-section*

25 mm (1 in)

Sand or sand/soil mixture

Timber

300 mm (12 in)

230 mm (9 in)

120 mm (5 in)

Soil

Drainage stones

Soil

Fig. 26 *Plan of dry-feed arrangement*

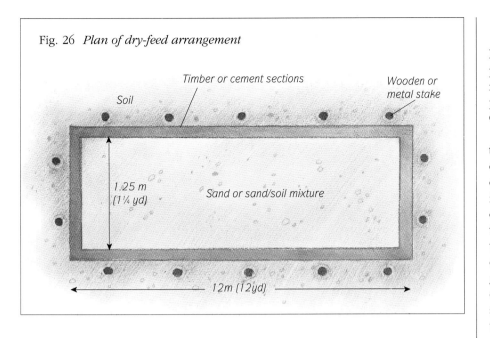

Soil

Timber or cement sections

Wooden or metal stake

1.25 m (1¼ yd)

Sand or sand/soil mixture

12m (12yd)

Feeding

If seeds have been planted in the prepared dry-feed bed, it will not be necessary to feed them with nutrient powder until they have germinated. Only water is necessary.

After the seedlings appear, feed them *weekly* with dry nutrient powder, applying it as thinly as possible down the rows of plants; then water in. Prevent dry powder from falling on to the plants as this will scorch the leaves. As the plants grow, continue the periodic application of the dry powder. Eventually, you will be guided by experience as to the frequency and amount of powder to apply. This period can be as long as three weeks, depending on the type of plant, its stage of growth and climatic conditions. It will do no harm to occasionally flood the beds with water to wash out any unused salts that have accumulated.

The main disadvantage of the dry-feed system is the labour involved in applying the dry powder. Furthermore, there is little or no control of pH, as there is when nutrient solution is fed to the plants.

stones, place a 230 mm (9 in) layer of growing medium. Builders' sand or a 50:50 mixture of soil and sand would be ideal. The important factor here is drainage. Only media affording efficient drainage should be used. For this reason, perlite and vermiculite would not be recommended.

5. Before planting, sprinkle a thin layer of nutrient powder over the surface of the medium. As a guide, use about 25 g per m² (1 oz per sq yd) of growing area. This means using about 375 g (11 oz) of plant food on a 15 m² (18 sq yd) bed. Water in well with a garden hose fitted with a fine spray rose.

Plant seeds or transplant seedlings as you would in soil. Adequate sunlight for the plants is important; they will receive sufficient food from their regular dry-feeds.

A five-course brick bed built against a wall can also be adapted for dry-feeding. The base course of bricks will need 38 mm (1½ in) gaps or weep holes, through which the excess water can drain away. Drainage stones are placed at the bottom of the bed, which is then topped up with growing medium to a depth of about 230 mm (9 in).

Almost all flowers and vegetables, and even fruits such as bananas, peaches, apples, currants, gooseberries and pears, may be successfully grown in these beds. The plants can be staked with bamboo canes, which is a standard practice; alternatively, an overhead system of wires and polypropylene twine can be rigged.

Swiss chard is a suitable crop for dry-feeding in sand

SUB-IRRIGATION IN GRAVEL

The main advantage of the sub-irrigation method is that there is a double change of oxygen around the plants' root system after completion of each pumping and drainage cycle.

A general outline of the system will be given here. Should you wish to go into the finer details of construction, operation and solution management, consult the author's definitive manual on this subject, entitled *Hydroponics: The Complete Guide to Gardening without Soil* (New Holland Publishers, London, 1994).

This system was devised by scientists at Purdue University in the United States. In its simplest form, its essential features are a *watertight container* (hydroponic bed) filled with *gravel*, a *nutrient solution reservoir* and an *electric pump*.

Construction

Any handy gardening enthusiast could build a hydroponic bed of this type. If necessary, one could supervise hired labour or even employ an outside contractor to do the job.

1. Select a sunny sight that is protected from the wind and lies in a north-south orientation along its length.

A hydroponic bed with brick walls

2. Cast the entire bed in concrete, providing for a length not greater than 50 m (55 yd) and a maximum width of 1.5 m (5 ft), which will allow the grower to comfortably reach the middle of the bed from either side

(see also step 6, this page). During casting, set a 200 mm (8 in) length of copper or PVC (32 mm [1¼ in] in diameter) into one end of the base.

Place strips of a rigid material, drilled with a series of holes, over the channel

3. Allow a depth of about 230 mm (9 in) – measured from the top of the wall to the base – and a fall of at least 20 mm (¾ in) from the sides to the central channel.

Before filling with gravel chip, place a layer of stones over the channel

4. Make provision for a 150 mm (6 in) wide drainage channel in the base and for a fall of 25 mm (1 in) from the far end to the pump end of the channel.

5. Place strips of a rigid material 230 mm (9 in) wide and 5 mm (¼ in) thick, drilled with a series of 3 mm (⅛ in) holes, over the length of the channel to serve as a cover.

6. As an alternative to casting the sides and end walls of the bed in concrete, lay two bricks on edge on the concrete slab. Plaster the brick wall thus made internally with a 3:1 mortar. Finish it off with an 18 mm (¾ in) coping.

7. Leave the whole structure for a few days to dry out. Then paint all the internal surfaces with a bitumen *emulsion* and finish off with a second coat of bitumen *solution* or one of the many proprietary rubberized paints to be found on the market.

8. Place a 38 mm (1½ in) layer of coarse stones 12–18 mm (½ – ¾ in) in diameter over the length of the drainage channel cover, to a width of about 450 mm (18 in). This is to prevent the finer gravel from blocking the holes in the cover.

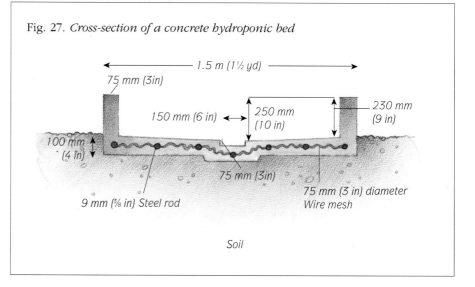

Fig. 27. *Cross-section of a concrete hydroponic bed*

1.5 m (1½ yd)

75 mm (3in)

150 mm (6 in)

250 mm (10 in)

230 mm (9 in)

100 mm (4 in)

75 mm (3in)

9 mm (⅜ in) Steel rod

75 mm (3 in) diameter Wire mesh

Soil

Fig. 28 *Transverse section, showing bed, reservoir and pump relationship*

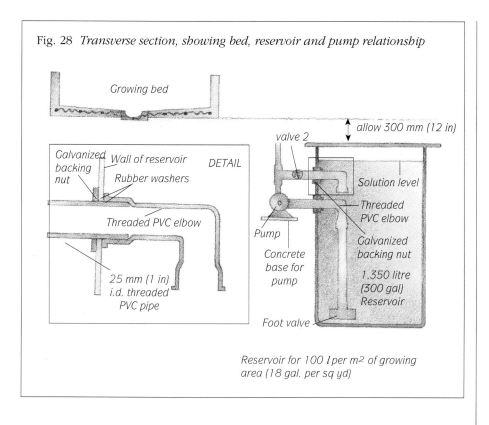

Growing bed

allow 300 mm (12 in)

valve 2

DETAIL

Galvanized backing nut

Wall of reservoir

Rubber washers

Threaded PVC elbow

25 mm (1 in) i.d. threaded PVC pipe

Solution level

Threaded PVC elbow

Galvanized backing nut

1,350 litre (300 gal) Reservoir

Pump

Concrete base for pump

Foot valve

Reservoir for 100 l per m² of growing area (18 gal. per sq yd)

Fig. 29 *Plan of bed, reservoir, pipeline, valves and pump*

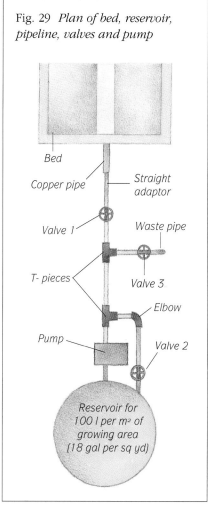

Bed

Copper pipe

Straight adaptor

Valve 1

Waste pipe

T- pieces

Valve 3

Elbow

Pump

Valve 2

Reservoir for 100 l per m² of growing area (18 gal per sq yd)

9. Fill the entire base of the bed with 3–6 mm (⅛–¼ in) gravel chip to within 12 mm (½ in) of the top.

10. Sink a reservoir of sufficient capacity for at least *100 litres per square metre of growing area* (18 gallons per square yd) in the ground so that the top of the reservoir is at least 300 mm (12 in) below the level of the base of the hydroponic bed.

11. Install an electric pump between the reservoir and the hydroponic bed just constructed.

12. Connect up an ancillary system of PVC pipes, elbows and T-pieces 25 mm (1 in) in diameter, and three gate valves. Details are shown in Fig. 28 and Fig. 29.

The inclusion of a *time-clock* and a *ball-float valve* attached to the water mains will make the system virtually automatic, but this is optional.

The nutrient solution is made up in the reservoir and pumped into the entrance pipe cast through the end

of the channel. From here it flows through the channel cover into the gravel, gradually rising to the surface. When the level of the liquid has reached about 25 mm (1 in) from the surface of the gravel, the pump is switched off – either by hand or by time-clock, if one has been installed. The liquid now flows back into the reservoir by gravity, completing the pumping cycle.

Any water lost by evaporation and transpiration is restored to the reservoir from the mains, either by hosepipe or by ball-float valve, if there is one. The pumping cycle is repeated daily using the same nutrient for two or three weeks.

Alternative methods of construction

1. A sub-irrigation system can be set up more cheaply using a 250 micron black polythene sheet. Support this around its periphery with mesh made from 5 mm (¼ in) diameter steel (used in the building industry) or sheets of a suitably rigid material.

The first step is to rough-dig the proposed area of the bed, making provision for the central channel. This can be made out of a 110 mm (4¼ in) diameter, heavy-duty, PVC drainage pipe, blocked off at one end. Drill 3 mm (⅛ in) holes over the top third of its circumference, along its entire length.

Black polythene sheet may be used as a liner for the hydroponic bed

The problem lies in joining the inlet (pump) end of the PVC pipe to the polythene sheet, and maintaining a waterproof seal. One way of doing this is to thread the end of the PVC pipe and then to secure it inside and outside using rubber seals and backing nuts.

Cut the polythene sheet to form a continuous internal lining, to cover the growing area to a depth of about 230 mm (9 in). This should be supported by a steel-mesh or other rigid framework buried in the ground. Fold the sheet in such a way as to ensure that the container remains watertight. It is very important to lay the base of the polythene sheet dead-level on the ground so that no substantial puddles of water will form in the bottom of the bed.

Position the PVC drainage pipe so that there is a fall of at least 25 mm (1 in) from the far end to the pump end – and make allowance for the 20 mm (¾ in) slope from the sides to the centre of the bed. Attach all ancillary pipes, elbows, T-pieces and valves as described in step 12, Fig. 28 and Fig. 29 on page 45.

One disadvantage of using a polythene liner is that it is relatively easily punctured by sharp objects, making it necessary to apply patches to the affected areas.

2. As an alternative to constructing a concrete slab or using a polythene liner just described, one could construct a base for the bed from 600 mm x 600 mm (2 ft x 2 ft) square 50 mm (2 in) thick pre-cast cement pavement slabs.

One half of the base of the bed will consist of concrete paving slabs laid side by side. Next to this layer of slabs lay a pre-cast drainage channel 150 mm (6 in) in diameter. Then lay the other half of the cement slabs parallel with the drainage channel (see Fig. 30).

A two-tier layer of bricks on edge for the end and side walls completes the hydroponic bed. All spaces between the cement slabs used to construct the base will have to be mortared and made waterproof using one of the many suitable compounds available on the market.

One disadvantage of this design is the possibility of fine cracks forming between the mortared bondings.

The phosphate treatment of calcareous growing media

Many sands and some gravels contain shell or limestone (calcium carbonate). These are said to be *calcareous*. If left untreated, the alkalinity caused by the limestone will affect the nutrient solution. The pH of the solution will rise and cause precipitation of some of the trace elements. Any new sand or gravel should be tested by adding hydrochloric (not sulphuric) acid to a small beaker containing a sample of the growing medium. An effervescence of gas indicates the presence of carbonates. The quantity can be roughly judged by the intensity and duration of the effervescence. If more than 10 per cent carbonate is judged to be present, the growing medium will have to be treated before use. The procedure is similar to that described on page 64 for the sterilization of the growing medium.

In place of a sterilizing agent, use a strong superphosphate solution. This is made by adding 1.5 kg (3¼ lb) of superphosphate (8.3% P) to 500 litres (110 gallons) of water in the reservoir. Mix for 30 minutes, then allow to stand for a few hours. Pump this solution into the gravel and allow it to stand overnight. Gradually the limestone and shell will become coated with an insoluble phosphate. Allow the spent superphosphate solution to drain away, then wash the gravel twice with plain water. The gravel is now ready for planting.

Calcareous dry-fed sand beds may also be treated with a superphosphate solution, should this become necessary. This, however, would have to be added in a solution, from above. After standing overnight, the bed should be washed with plain water at least three times, to leach the excess salts away. The procedure is not as simple or efficient as it is with sub-irrigation.

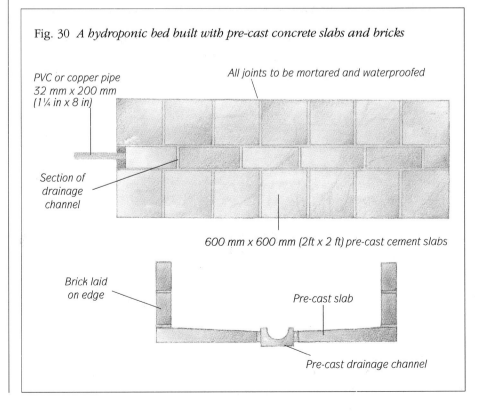

Fig. 30 *A hydroponic bed built with pre-cast concrete slabs and bricks*

PVC or copper pipe 32 mm x 200 mm (1¼ in x 8 in)

All joints to be mortared and waterproofed

Section of drainage channel

600 mm x 600 mm (2ft x 2 ft) pre-cast cement slabs

Brick laid on edge

Pre-cast slab

Pre-cast drainage channel

CHAPTER EIGHT

GROWING YOUR OWN SEEDLINGS

A seed-tray full of healthy seedlings is a pleasurable sight to any gardener. It is also the first step towards a sturdy, mature plant. Since this is the critical stage in the plant's life, it is vital to ensure a successful start.

SEED GERMINATION

For successful germination, seeds must have adequate *warmth* and *moisture* at all times and must never be allowed to dry out.

After a seed is planted, the hard, dry outer seed-coat begins to absorb moisture and soften. At just the right temperature, and if sufficient moisture is present, the surge of life begins within, triggering a strong physical force. In most plants this results in the incipient yellowish seed leaves known as *cotyledons* pushing out through the softened seed-coat into the growing medium. When they come into contact with sunlight, photosynthesis begins and they become green.

While the leaves are pushing up and out, the embryo root or *radicle* spreads through the medium, absorbing water and nourishment for the tiny seedling.

The seed is not only a storehouse of potential energy, but, initially, also contains a complete, though limited, food supply. For this reason it is not necessary (though also not harmful, for that matter) to give the seed nutrient solution *prior* to germination. Plain water will do.

The seed-tray

The seed-tray may be of any shape or size but is usually rectangular and 70–100 mm (2¾–4 in) in depth. There is a large variety of plastic

A seed tray full of Syncarpha paniculata *seedlings*

seed-trays made of PVC or expanded polystyrene on the market. The latter is excellent for seed germination since it is a good insulator.

A *fruit-box* lined with plastic sheet or a double layer of kraft (bituminized) paper can also be used. Punch a few holes in the bottom for drainage purposes. It is good practice, though not essential, to include a shallow layer of drainage stones before filling with a growing medium.

The ideal growing medium

Fresh horticultural vermiculite of the correct pH is an excellent medium for germinating seeds, and has the following advantages:

• maximum percentage germination (strike) of seeds
• the superior water-holding capacity of vermiculite means that there is less chance of it drying out; drying out can be fatal to germinating seeds
• minimum danger of shock and wilting after transplanting
• *fresh* vermiculite is sterile, hence there is minimum danger from soil-borne disease
• an absence of soil-borne weeds

Although the focus in this chapter will be on vermiculite, one must not overlook the other media, like washed river sand, perlite and sawdust in which seedlings can be grown. It should be borne in mind that different growing media will require subtle differences in handling.

Preparation

To prepare the container, follow the step-by-step instructions given on page 26. Omit step 2 unless you are using metal trays or some other material requiring painting. Modify step 3 by placing squares of *moistened* nylon mesh over the drainage holes; you may omit step 4.

Buy only fresh seeds sold by reputable dealers. So many failures can be traced to old, non-viable seed, that to try and economize in this manner would be foolhardy! This advice is so important that it is worth repeating – ALWAYS SOW FRESH SEED.

It is a good idea to soak seeds with very hard seed coats, for example, sweet peas, in water overnight, prior to planting. This will help to soften the outer coat and thereby facilitate germination.

Feeding

A watering-can fitted with a fine rose is recommended for applying nutrient solutions.

Water the vermiculite periodically with water or half-strength solution (plain water is perfectly adequate but half-strength solution will do no harm) until the seedlings germinate. Avoid over-watering as this can encourage the development of fungal diseases in the root system, of which the destructive 'damping off' is only too familiar. Try to water suf-

The 'Speedling' system allows mass production of seedlings

ficiently to produce a 'wetted and wrung out sponge' condition.

Following the manufacturer's instructions (if you are using a commercial hydroponic nutrient powder), gradually increase the nutrient to full-strength about one week after germination.

The length of the dormant period before germination can vary greatly, depending on the type of seed. Some will germinate in three days, others in three weeks or more. A lot depends on temperature conditions. For example, under favourable conditions a tomato seed will germinate within ten days, but this period could extend to three weeks when conditions are less favourable.

It is important that seed-beds are never allowed to dry out completely; nor should they be subjected to temperature extremes.

WEATHER CONDITIONS

Light rain will do no harm to seedlings but heavy rain can cause physical damage. If heavy rain occurs frequently in your area it will be necessary to provide your seedlings with temporary shelter.

Germinate and grow your seedlings in sunlight, for lack of light will always produce weak, spindly seedlings. However, in very hot, harsh sun, some shade may be beneficial. Under these conditions, a 3 mm (⅛ in) wire-mesh screen or shadecloth on a wooden frame will provide shade and partial shelter to newly germinated seedlings.

During spells of very cold weather it is advisable to move the seed-trays indoors or to a warm place until germination commences. This should only be a temporary measure, however, and after germination the seed-trays should immediately be moved back to their permanent position in the sunlight.

To avoid delayed germination caused by very cold weather, use a heated germination frame where temperature can be controlled.

TRANSPLANTING

Seedlings can be thinned out in the normal way and the surplus, if required, transplanted into more seed-trays.

Transplanting has already been discussed in Chapter Four. There is,

however, one very distinct advantage that vermiculite has over other growing media, especially with respect to transplanting, that is worth detailing here.

After removing the seedling from the seed-tray, a clump of vermiculite will remain attached to the well-developed root system, ensuring a built-in moisture 'reservoir', and a readily available nutrient supply. The significance of this is *minimum setback or wilting of the transplant in its new environment*. Such an advantage hardly needs stressing.

COMMERCIAL SEEDLINGS

No chapter on seedlings would be complete without mention of the 'Speedling' system for large-scale commercial production of seedlings. This is a patented method devised in the United States for mass production, based on the familiar method of seedling production using the 'plug-growing' system.

The essential feature of this system is the special plastic tray, the base of which consists of a series of inverted pyramids. These are designed to prevent intertwining of rootlets. After development of each seedling in its own pyramid, they are easily removed manually from the tray by their stems. There is no shock and the transplants grow into vigorous plants.

The growing medium is usually a mixture of composted organic and inorganic materials. The trays vary in size, from those containing 72 cavities to those with 200 cavities, and are either mechanically or manually filled with growing medium. The seeds are also inserted by machine and the seeded trays placed on racks under shadecloth. Overhead sprays, which are usually mechanized, keep the seedlings moist with dilute nutrient solution at pre-determined intervals until germination.

Colourful carnations (Dianthus chinensis)

The 'perpetual flowering' Dianthus carophyllus *growing in gravel*

Gladiolus

This flower, noted for its magnificent and lofty spikes, requires less attention than the carnation. It is comparatively easy to grow and remains a favourite amongst gardeners. Commercial growers are more concerned with producing corms after disposing of the flower spikes.

PLANTING AND MAINTENANCE Gladioli corms can be obtained from nurseries, gardening stores or through mail order catalogues in various sizes, ranging from small (9–12 mm [½ in]) to large (38–50 mm [1½–2 in]). The home gardener is advised to buy medium-sized corms of about 25 mm (1 in).

To prepare for planting, dig shallow trenches about 75 mm (3 in) deep and 150 mm (6 in) apart, in the growing medium of your choice. Place the corms in a straight line in the trenches, no more than 12 mm (½ in) apart. Cover over with growing medium. At this spacing, a 1.25 m x 12 m (4 ft x 38 ft) bed would take about 2,800 medium-sized corms.

In favourable weather, the first green shoot will appear above the surface within ten days and can grow at the rate of 25 mm (1 in) each day. Feed only when necessary, at a pH of 6.0. It is important not to over-water since a constant high moisture content in the growing medium could lead to *fungal rot*.

Gladioli corms can be planted at any time from the end of winter to mid-summer (in temperate climes, wait until the danger of frost is over). The first flower spikes will be picked 80 to 90 days after planting. If planting is staggered in two-weekly cycles, flowers may be obtained for almost six months of the year.

PESTS, DISEASES AND OTHER PROBLEMS The four main problems that affect gladioli are the *gladiolus fly, thrips, fungal rot* and *rust*. Chapter Ten provides more detailed information on dealing with these problems.

The long spikes are very vulnerable to wind, so some staking system is essential in windy areas. One method is to arrange stakes on either side of the end plants in each row. Tie cord to each stake to provide a two-cord support for every plant in the row. Horizontal sets of cords can be arranged at spacings of 230 mm (9 in) between each set

Chrysanthemum

This plant is a member of the vast family of daisies known as the *Compositae,* offering the grower a wide range – from the enormous giant chrysanthemums, to the tiny pompon varieties.

Chrysanthemum growing is not difficult if the natural flowering season is followed. However, all-year-round growing is a highly specialized form of flower cultivation.

PLANTING AND MAINTENANCE As with the carnation, flowers can be produced from seed. The serious grower, however, uses cuttings for propagating true-to-type flowers for shows and exhibitions.

Cuttings strike easily in sand and are best taken in early spring from the sucker growths – those shoots with a small cluster of roots found near ground level on an old crown. Trim the cutting by removing the two side leaves and squaring off just below the joint (see Fig. 31).

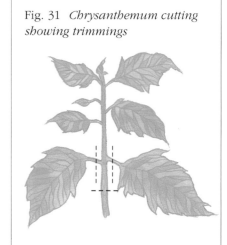

Fig. 31 *Chrysanthemum cutting showing trimmings*

Dip the cutting in a root-growth hormone powder and water with half-strength solution until roots have formed (three to four weeks). Space about 450 mm (18 in) apart in the hydroponic bed.

For details on stopping and the pinching out of the 'break buds', consult a specialist book on chrysanthemum cultivation. This will also provide information on how light and temperature can influence flower production.

PESTS AND DISEASES Many serious pests and diseases affect chrysanthemums, including *aphids, leaf miner, powdery mildew, rust, leaf spot, grey mould, root rot, white rust* and *damping-off.* (See Chapter Ten.)

Chrysanthemums grown hydroponically in sand

Snapdragon *(Antirrhinum)*

The snapdragon – originally a Mediterranean, summer-flowering perennial, and now grown mostly as an annual – will provide the gardener with colourful flowers for many months of the year.

It is readily propagated from seed, which can initially be planted in vermiculite seed-trays. Seeds may be germinated all year round, though late summer for winter-flowering varieties and spring for summer-flowering varieties, are the best times to sow.

When the seedlings have grown to two-leaf pairs and have reached a height of about 60 mm (2 in), they may be transplanted into their permanent position in the hydroponic bed.

PESTS, DISEASES AND OTHER PROBLEMS
As the snapdragon is particularly susceptible to *rust*, regular prophylactic spraying is essential. (See Chapter Ten.)

Some varieties grow tall, so proper staking is essential.

Rose

The title 'queen of flowers' must surely belong to the rose, a flower as old as history itself.

Originally from China, the modern rose is the result of a blend of European and Eastern varieties.

The preparation of soil for rose planting is a vast subject, but using the hydroponic method it is as simple to grow a rose as it is a tomato.

We can conveniently divide the many types and varieties of rose into three broad classes, namely:

- the Hybrid Teas
- the Polyanthas
- the Floribundas

The Hybrid Tea or common rose, seen in most gardens and grown for pleasure or exhibition, is what we shall describe here.

PLANTING Young rose bushes, usually obtained from nurseries, consist of a *stock*, which are the roots with a short stem, on to which the *scion* has been grafted. The stem extends up to 50 mm (2 in) above the roots where the scion or potential bud-stock commences.

At the end of winter or the beginning of spring, plant the roots into a 450 mm (18 in) wide and 150 mm (6 in) deep hole in the growing medium (in soil the hole is dug to a depth of about 400 mm [16 in]). Roses do particularly well in gravel or a coarse sand. There is a short dormant period in mid-summer when they may also be planted.

Place the plant in the hole and spread the roots. Fill in with growing medium and lightly firm down. Irrigate immediately with a general hydroponic nutrient at a pH of 6.0.

A 1.25 m x 12 m (4 ft x 38 ft) bed will accommodate at least 36 rose bushes in two rows, positioned about 300 mm (12 in) from the sides, and spaced 600 mm (2 ft) from one another within a row.

The newly planted bush will soon establish itself and, before long, the original bare branches will be transformed into a mass of green leaves and young, developing buds.

PRUNING After nearly a year's growth, with almost a perpetual showing of blooms, the dormant months will arrive. Now is the time to prune. This should not be carried out too early or too late. Mid-winter is the time of year for this important operation, but avoid frosty weather.

The aim of pruning is two-fold: first, to remove weak, dead or misdirected growth, and second, to encourage an optimum shape for the bush. An ideal shape is the umbrella.

It must also be borne in mind that hydroponic growth tends to be vigorous, so that more severe pruning will be necessary than would be the case with roses growing in soil.

Always try to cut a 45° angle parallel with, and about 6 mm (¼ in)

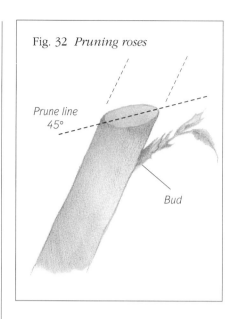

Fig. 32 *Pruning roses*

Prune line 45°

Bud

above, an *outward-facing* bud (see Fig. 32). A sharp pair of secateurs will make a clean cut. The reason for choosing an outward-facing bud is that this will encourage the new shoot to grow outwards.

Immediately after pruning, wipe away the sap that may have oozed out of the cut, and paint the newly exposed surface with aluminium paint or other sealant. This is done to discourage fungal die-back.

After pruning, the bush will consist of a neat, roughly circular spread of bare branches, each with buds waiting to develop when spring arrives.

DISBUDDING The reason for disbudding is to encourage fewer but more vigorous blooms, since the buds are all competing for the same nourishment. Growers who wish to exhibit their blooms pay particular attention to disbudding, as both bloom size and quality are enhanced as a result.

PESTS, DISEASES AND OTHER PROBLEMS
Aphids are most persistent and can thrive in their thousands around new shoots and buds. Be constantly on the look-out for these pests, as they proliferate extremely speedily and are very destructive. Fortunately, they are easily destroyed.

In many countries *beetles* and *caterpillars* are also pests that the gardener should guard against.

The three main fungal diseases that affect roses are *black spot*, *rust* and *mildew*. (See Chapter Ten.)

Because the hydroponic growing bed is relatively shallow, it is most important that roses should be supported with bamboo stakes.

As roses are perennials it will not be possible to sterilize the growing medium during the period that it is occupied by the roses.

Other flowers

There is virtually no limit to the variety of flowers that can be grown using the hydroponic method. Commercial growing, however, depends on marketing factors, and apart from the obvious examples discussed in this chapter, there are probably many other types of flowers that one could grow for sale. The *Anthurium* comes to mind as one possibility. *Gerbera* is a most attractive flower too, and in The Netherlands many hectares of these are grown in glasshouses on rockwool using the overhead drip method of irrigation.

So why not go out and buy a packet of seeds of your favourite flower and plant them? Don't be afraid to experiment. The hydroponic method allows you wide scope. Try different media. Vary your irrigation schedules. Whatever you do, you are bound to be delighted with the results.

VEGETABLES

Vegetables are essential for our health, providing us with a cheap source of minerals and vitamins. City dwellers who buy their vegetables mainly from supermarkets and other outlets are probably unaware that some of these will have been grown by the hydroponic method.

While it is true that the ubiquitous vegetable plot is still a feature of many homes, home hydroponic growers are increasing in number. Although vegetables may be grown on balconies, the opportunities for growing are limited by considerations of space and often also of light.

We have already given some estimate of what quantities of vegetables the home grower can expect to produce in an area measuring 15 m² (18 sq yd). Table 2 shows the numbers of each plant one can grow in this area at any one time.

When one takes into account the fact that hydroponic vegetables mature more quickly than those planted in soil, the argument in

Table 2	
Vegetable	Approximate no. of plants in 15 m² (18 sq yd)
Tomato	40
Lettuce	160
Cucumber	30
Peppers	60

favour of hydroponic production becomes even more compelling.

Probably the two most popular vegetables grown by this method are the cucumber and the tomato.

Just as easily grown in hydroponic beds are Swiss chard (spinach), the pepper (capsicum) family, celery, many varieties of lettuce, as well as the below-ground crops such as onion, radish, beetroot and potato.

Tomato *(Lycopersicon esculentum)*

Strictly speaking, the tomato is a fruit – once thought to be poisonous – but in keeping with common perceptions, we shall consider it a vegetable. This plant is probably one of the easiest and most commonly grown by the hydroponic method.

Belonging to the same family as the potato, the tomato originates in South America. It can be grown as a vine (indeterminate) or bush (determinate). The former is common in glasshouse production, the latter in field growing.

Essentially a sun-loving plant, the tomato grows well in temperatures ranging from 21–27 °C (70–81 °F). It also grows well in temperate zones at temperatures of 15–26 °C (60–79 °F) when under glass.

PLANTING AND MAINTENANCE

Generally, planting can begin in early spring. Seedlings are raised in trays, or seed may be planted directly into the hydroponic bed. Under optimum conditions germination can commence in six days.

In The Netherlands many hectares of Gerbera *are grown in rockwool*

In some countries, seeds are sown individually or pricked out into 30 mm (1¼ in) cubes of rockwool. About a week later these will have been transplanted into 75 mm (3 in) rockwool cubes, which are then placed in gullies.

Feed seedlings with a general nutrient mixture at a pH of 6.0. After three to four weeks, when the seedling is starting to produce its second pair of leaves (excluding the seed leaves), it will be time to transplant them into their permanent positions in the hydroponic bed. At this stage the seedling should be 60–75 mm (2–3 in) high. Place them into the growing medium almost up to the two seed leaves and at least 500 mm (20 in) apart. A 1.25 m x 12 m (4 ft x 38 ft) bed will easily take 40 plants in two rows running the length of the bed.

When using the hydroponic method for growing tomatoes, some support of the vine is essential. Attach the main stems to 2 m (6 ft) bamboo stakes with plastic ties. The bamboo stakes are themselves secured to overhead wires. Alternatively, use polypropylene twine. Tie a 20 mm (¾ in) loop of twine around the main stem of the developing plant when it is about 150 mm (6 in) high. This will make allowance for the rapidly increasing diameter of the main stem.

Using a slip knot, secure the other end of the twine to overhead wires, which should be at least 1.8 m (6 ft) above the surface of the growing medium. This allows for slack in accommodating the rapidly increasing weight of the fruit-laden plant, which one gradually twists around the twine.

STOPPING The commercial grower invariably grows the indeterminate variety of tomato (for example, Meran, Pronto, Estrella, Liberto, Diego, Jamaico), keeping the plant to a single main stem. This is achieved by *pinching out* all the new shoots, starting in the axils of

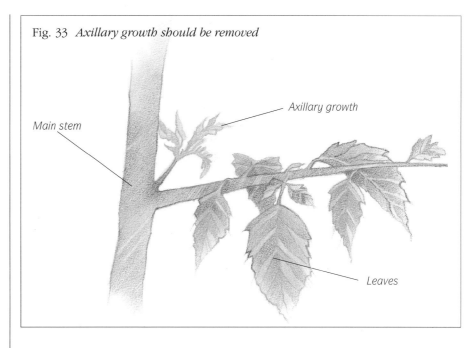

Fig. 33 *Axillary growth should be removed*

Main stem

Axillary growth

Leaves

the leaves, which are known as axillary growth (see Fig. 33). It is best to do this when the shoots are quite small, since there is less risk of botrytis at this stage.

As growth progresses, the plant will produce its first *truss*. This is a short stem full of flowers which ultimately develop into the fruit. After about eight trusses have formed, remove the terminal growing point two leaves above the top truss and allow a basal side shoot to grow on.

You may of course prefer to grow the determinate type of tomato bush, in which case it is not necessary to stop or pinch out growth. Obtain advice on the cultivars in current use from your nursery or seed merchant.

DEFOLIATING When indeterminate tomatoes are grown hydroponically, there is usually an abundance of vegetation because of the ready availability of nutrients. This poses the question of whether or not to prune the excess. Even among the experts, opinion is divided on defoliation, which involves cutting off the lower branches from the main stem. This has the effect of minimizing certain fungal infections and allowing more light to reach the bottom

trusses, so they ripen more quickly.

It is commercial practice in some parts of Europe to defoliate the plant as the fruit is picked off the trusses. Our recommendation is gradual defoliation up to a height of 750 mm (30 in) above the surface of the growing medium. Ensure that the leaf is cut off as close as possible to the main stem.

HARVESTING AND YIELDS Within eight weeks of planting the seed, the first truss should appear; the first ripe fruit can be picked within another six to eight weeks, although this will depend on climatic conditions.

In an unprotected temperate climate tomatoes can be harvested for seven months of the year if stagger-planted. In heated tunnels or greenhouses, however, it is possible to produce two full crops over a period of twelve to fourteen months or a single long-season crop over eleven months (allowing one month to clear out, clean up and start again).

A yield of 6–8 kg (13–17½ lb) per plant is not unusual. With a planting density of 2.7 plants per m² (2.3 plants per sq yd) this means a yield of approximately 240 kg per 15 m² (530 lb per 18 sq yd).

PESTS AND DISEASES The tomato is host to a wide variety of pests and diseases, which will be briefly described here.

There are the fungal diseases of which the *blights* (*Macrosporia solanum* and *Phytophthora infestans*) are common. Early and late varieties can best be prevented by spraying (see Appendix 6). *Septoria leaf spot* is another fungal disease. *Fusarium wilt* attacks the roots, eventually causing the plant to die back. This should not be confused with *bacterial wilt*, which causes sudden wilting in the tomato. The latter, of bacterial origin, is not often encountered in hydroponic growing, but can be the cause of rapid decay and death.

Eelworm, a nematode that invades the roots of the tomato plant, is an extremely troublesome pest. The aim should be prevention, since eradication is difficult. The main effect of this infestation is lower yields. It will be necessary to sterilize the growing medium before the next planting (see page 64).

The other three pests are *whitefly*, *red spider* and *caterpillars*. All three of these can be controlled and, in most cases, eliminated.

Another problem is *blossom-end rot*. This manifests itself as a flat, dried-up, black to dark-brown area that sometimes forms on the bottom of the tomato fruit where the blossom has dropped off. This is not a disease, but a nutritional disorder that is thought to be related to a calcium deficiency during fruit formation. The condition can occur as a result of temporary water stress or during a spell of hot or windy weather. The problem can be limited to negligible proportions by correct management.

English Cucumber
(*Cucumis sativus*)

This popular salad crop is a member of the very large cucurbit family, which includes the melons, pumpkin

The English cucumber is a popular crop with hydroponic growers

and squash, and grows well in warm climates. Like most cucurbits, the cucumber has separate male and female flowers growing on the same plant. Since only the female flower gives a fruit, modern breeding has encouraged production of the all-female plant.

Some well-known hybrids are Pepinex, Pandorex, Sandra, Farbiola, Corona, Primera, Bronco, Jessica and Uniflora. Ask for advice on current varieties and their characteristics at your local nursery or seed merchant.

PLANTING AND MAINTENANCE The cucumber is far more sensitive to temperature fluctuation than the tomato. The ideal range for growing is from a minimum of 16 °C (61 °F) to a maximum of 26 °C (79 °F). Too high a temperature or too vast a fluctuation in temperature can result in curved fruits as well as abortion of young cucumbers.

Seeds should be sown directly into sand or gravel, where germination will be rapid at an optimum temperature of 27 °C (81 °F). The seeds should be set about 600 mm (24 in) apart in the beds and can be staked using polypropylene twine attached to overhead wires.

Cucumber plants require a slightly more concentrated nutrient solution than tomatoes. An EC of 2,500 microsiemens and a pH of 6.0 is recommended (see page 36).

STOPPING Keep the plant to a single main stem by removing all side shoots, until it has grown to a height of 1.8 m (6 ft). Then remove the growing point and allow two diametrically opposed side shoots to grow on, effectively producing an umbrella shape (see Fig. 34). These laterals, as they are called, grow up to the horizontal wire, along it and then downwards. The bulk of the crop is produced by the laterals.

Alternatively, use vertical cordons, inclined cordons or arch training – specialist publications will give you more details.

HARVESTING AND YIELDS
The first cucumber can be picked within ten weeks of sowing and a total crop of 25–40 cucumbers per plant can be expected. Both flavour and quality are excellent.

In intensive glasshouse production, each plant – at the height of the season – will produce one cucumber per day.

The modern F1 hybrid has seedless fruits that are usually picked at a length of 300–400 mm (12–16 in). At this stage they should be uniform in colour, fairly straight, thin-skinned, and can be eaten without peeling.

PESTS AND DISEASES The *whitefly* thrives on the underside of the large leaves of the cucumber. Unless the grower is alert, this infestation can become very troublesome.

Another very destructive pest is the *red spider mite* which can destroy a plant in a very short space of time. Both of these, however, can be controlled with the correct spraying schedule.

The main fungal diseases that affect the cucumber are *powdery mildew* and *downy mildew*, both being extremely destructive. (See Chapter Ten.)

Fig. 34 *Training cucumbers*

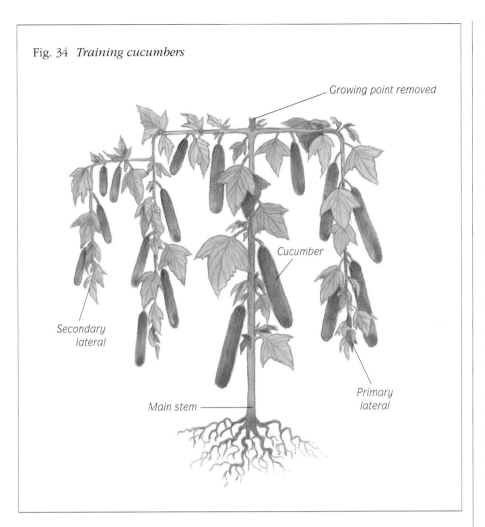

PLANTING AND MAINTENANCE Lettuces are best started in seed-trays; germination can be expected within ten days. When the second pair of leaves is about 25 mm (1 in) in size, transplant the seedling into its final position in the hydroponic bed, allowing at least 300 mm (12 in) between plants. It is best to do this towards evening or to wait for cool, cloudy weather. In hot, sunny climates a temporary shade cover in the form of a shade-cap will be beneficial. A 1.25 m x 12 m (4 ft x 38 ft) bed will accommodate about 160 plants at this spacing.

It is advisable to stagger the planting so as to ensure a continuous supply of fresh lettuce.

A general feed at a pH of 6.5 is recommended. If using the dry-feed method (see Chapter Seven) allow more space between the lettuce.

PESTS AND DISEASES *Caterpillars*, *aphids* and *snails* are pests that the grower will have to counter with the appropriate remedies. *Leaf spot* and *crown rot* are the main diseases that affect lettuce. (See Chapter Ten.)

Sweet Peppers
(*Capsicum annuum*)

Sweet peppers, which are also known as *paprika*, particularly in central Europe, are not related to the tropical peppers of the East. They thrive in warm conditions similar to those favoured by the tomato, to which they are related. Modern F1 hybrids produce very attractive bell-shaped fruits in vivid green, red and yellow. Chillies are also members of this family.

Orobelle is one of the bright canary-yellow varieties, while *Indra* has an equally vivid red colour. Both are somewhat sweet to the taste. *Californian Wonder* is a well-known green variety that is not as sweet as the first two varieties mentioned. Apart from their nutritious addition to any salad, the three varieties grown together will make an extremely attractive visual display in any garden.

Lettuce (*Latuca sativa*)

Along with the tomato, lettuce is a nutritious, attractive and indispensable salad crop. Clean, crisp heads, maturing in eight weeks or less in the warm months, are very easily grown in hydroponic beds filled with sand or gravel. Many supermarkets stock lettuces that have been grown hydroponically.

Essentially a cool-weather crop, lettuce may be cultivated throughout the year, but will have to be shaded during the heat of the summer months. The optimum growing range is 13–24 °C (65–75°F).

There are four main classes of lettuce, namely *loose-leaf, cos, butterhead* and *crisp*. Butterhead lettuce is very popular in Europe and is finding increasing acceptance in other parts of the world. One of the best-known crisp varieties, characterized by its prominent mid-rib, is *Great Lakes*, which was originally bred to withstand warm climatic conditions.

Lettuce mature in 8 weeks or less during the warmer months

PLANTING AND MAINTENANCE While easy to grow, the seed of the pepper takes time to germinate and is somewhat slow to mature. Germination can take up to four weeks after sowing, although – at 18 °C (65 °F) – seedlings will be big enough to transplant at around two weeks.

The developing bush requires very little attention, apart from periodic feedings, at a pH of 6.0. The plant itself is woody and somewhat brittle when laden with fruit, which are ready for picking about four months after sowing (or three months under protection). Peppers are prolific bearers and should be harvested regularly, preferably by cutting the fruit off the bush with sharp secateurs. Whatever variety is being cultivated, all pass through an initial green stage before changing to their final colour on ripening.

PESTS AND DISEASES The capsicum family is relatively free of pests and diseases. Should you totally neglect them, however, the ubiquitous *whitefly* is one pest that will very soon establish itself in great numbers on the underside of the leaves. (See Chapter Ten.)

Peas *(Pisum sativum)*

Like lettuce, peas are comparatively easy to grow in sand or gravel. They grow best in the cool part of the year. Mature hydroponically grown peas are so sweet that they can almost be eaten uncooked, straight from the pods. One well-known and trusted cultivar is *Greenfeast*.

PLANTING AND MAINTENANCE Place the seed directly into the beds, at a depth of about 25 mm (1 in), allowing spaces of 90 mm (3½ in) between plants. In order to obtain some continuity of production, it is a good idea to stagger-plant every two or three weeks.

It is most important to stake the rows of pea plants, especially in

Any herb can be grown by the hydroponic method

windy areas. A trellis or rot-proof netting, which will give the tendrils good anchorage, will be effective for this purpose.

It takes about twelve weeks for the first pods to become ripe enough for harvesting. Where possible, twice-weekly picking is advised.

PESTS AND DISEASES The pea is attacked by a variety of pests of which *aphids*, *thrips*, *leaf miners* and *red spider* are the main ones.

Warm, moist conditions will encourage *powdery* and *downy mildew*, to which this plant is particularly susceptible.

All the above can be successfully controlled with a systematic spraying schedule. (See Chapter Ten.)

Other vegetables

Five examples of vegetables that can be grown successfully have been described here, but there is almost no limit to what can be grown.

You may prefer to grow one of the root crops such as radish, onion, beetroot or carrot, or possibly a leaf crop of Swiss chard, cabbage, Brussels sprouts or broccoli. Whatever your choice, you will be delighted with the results.

HERBS

Hydroponics offers an opportunity to grow your favourite herbs in the kitchen without too much trouble.

The techniques for hydroponic growing, either in a window-box or a larger bed, have already been described in Chapters Four and Seven. All that remains to be done is to purchase packets of seed and follow instructions.

When growing herbs indoors it is essential that *adequate light is always provided*. If this is neglected, spindly plants reaching out for the light will result, leading to failure.

Although a wide variety of herbs can be grown hydroponically in a window-box, one is somewhat limited in terms of size. Many of the herbs grow into large bushes, so if grown indoors, frequent pruning will be necessary. This constraint will obviously not apply to the outdoor grower.

The choice of what to grow will depend on the individual, but practically any known herb, including the following, can be cultivated: basil*, bay, chervil*, chives*, dill*, fennel, mint*, marjoram*, parsley*, rosemary, sage*, sorrel, tarragon* or thyme. (Those followed by an asterisk can also be grown indoors.)

Sweet peppers (Capsicum species) *are prolific bearers*

CHAPTER TEN

PESTS AND DISEASES

Whatever method of raising crops the grower may choose, there are bound to be problems of some kind. Perhaps those most frequently encountered are the insect pests and diseases that attack the plants, particularly in the mature stages of their growth.

Among the insect pests are aphids, beetles, caterpillars, the minute flies, mites and the various scales.

The manifold fungal infections are common diseases that attack most plants. Diseases of bacterial or viral origin, though less common, can be equally destructive.

Banish the notion that hydroponics somehow endows plants with some mystical immunity to the above! This is quite false. They are prey to the same range of pests and diseases as plants grown in soil, but there is one important difference. Certain dis-

Pretty beetles belie their destructive habits

In some countries locusts are a pest

eases are innately soil-borne and once the soil is infected, it is not an easy task to eliminate the invasive fungus or bacterium. In the hydroponic method – if one is using sub-irrigation – one starts with a freshly sterilized growing medium, pumps, pipelines and reservoir. The chance of disease similar to the soil-borne variety being present is thus eliminated at the outset.

It is a well-known and accepted fact that a healthy organism will be better able to withstand disease than a less healthy one. Hydroponically grown plants have every chance of being healthy.

The finer details of spraying plants against insects and diseases will be found in most gardening manuals. Our intention here is to discuss the broad principles of spraying, mentioning the main classes of pests and diseases, and suggesting a systematic scheme for their prevention or cure.

The number of pests and diseases, as well as remedies for them, are so numerous, that the average gardener is more often than not bewildered by the combinations and permutations in this field. There are seemingly as many different sprays, and even several of identical chemical types under different trade names, as there are pests and diseases.

How then can the home gardener be expected to make some sense out of all this apparently confusing information?

In the sections that follow, pests and diseases have been divided into a few broad types. The remedies for these have been kept to a minimum of three basic and four specific sprays, together with some available trade names, listed in Appendix 6. These seven types of spray make it possible to control just about all the pests and diseases the average gardener is likely to encounter.

Bugs are easily controlled by spraying

Voracious caterpillars emerge from the eggs of moths

TYPES OF PESTS

Insect pests can be conveniently divided into two main groups, namely *chewing* insects and *sucking* insects. Table 3 lists some well-known examples of each.

Table 3

Chewing	Sucking
Beetles	Ants
Caterpillars	Aphids
Crickets	Bugs
Cutworms	Fruit flies
Grasshoppers	Mites
Grubs	Scale
Locusts	insects
Moths	Thrips
Slugs and snails	Whitefly
Worms	

Chewing insects

These pests are responsible for the destruction of flowers, fruit, leaves, stems and roots of plants by chewing or nibbling them away. They are particularly destructive and, if irreparable damage is to be avoided, must be ruthlessly and completely destroyed. A good example of this type of insect is the 'looper' caterpillar, which makes its way into the tomato fruit, thus drastically reducing the edible crop.

CUTWORMS live just under the surface of the growing medium, and are very destructive, especially to tender seedlings. Several cutworms attack above-ground plants as well as roots. Unless you eradicate them when detected, it can be rather a laborious process to remove them completely.

The sub-irrigation method of hydroponics, however, offers the home grower a unique method of eliminating every cutworm that may find its way into the gravel. True, their numbers are not likely to be as great as they would be in soil, but they certainly do occur.

To eradicate them, simply flood the gravel bed until the liquid is about level with the surface of the gravel. Within a short space of time every cutworm will either have been drowned by the liquid, or have found its way to the surface where it can be easily removed. Complete success is assured with this method.

Sucking insects

These pests are generally smaller than chewing insects. They live on the plant tissue, which they damage by sucking out the sap. If not controlled, they cause discoloration of the tissue, leading to the eventual death of the plant. The red spider mite, which lives on cucumber leaves, is a dreaded member of this group.

TYPES OF DISEASES

Diseases can be more difficult to control than insects. First, they are not always easy to diagnose, and secondly, once established on the host plant, they are very difficult to eliminate.

It is especially for the second reason that the main aim of spraying plants against disease is prevention rather than cure. Almost all commercial crop-raising, hydroponic or otherwise, requires a prophylactic spray programme, as opposed to contact spraying, which works for insect pests as these are usually visible.

Diseases may be divided into *fungal, bacterial* and *viral* types.

Black spot is caused by a fungus

Sooty mould on citrus leaves

Fungal diseases

These are by far the most common and are caused by the growth of a *fungus*. The spores of fungi, which might be compared with the seeds of plants, float freely in the atmosphere. They thrive in warm, moist conditions and, after settling on a host plant, send out a *mycelium* (like the stem and leaves of an ordinary plant). This can take the form of visible, velvet-like, white, black, red, green or blue spots and patches.

The fungus is a parasite that draws nourishment from the host plant. If not prevented or controlled in the

Rust is a prevalent fungal disease

Table 4

Fungal	Bacterial	Viral
Black spot	Canker	Leaf
Brown patch	Crown gall	mosaic
Blights	Wilt	Bunchy
Damping off	Soft rot	top
Die-back		Flower
Mildews		breaking
Moulds		
Rots		
Rusts		
Wilt		

very early stages of infection, fungal diseases will soon kill the plant. The *Irish potato blight* is a well-known example of a fungal disease.

Bacterial diseases

These are, fortunately, less common than fungal diseases, though they are highly destructive when they do occur. They are caused by microscopic organisms found in seed or soil, which multiply extremely rapidly, causing death or decay within hours. The bacteria can be spread by insects or by the wind.

Very little can be done to control bacterial disease, short of removing and destroying affected plants.

Viral diseases

These are even rarer than bacterial diseases and are not necessarily terminal. They show up in blotches, streaks or mosaics on the leaves, and often reduce yields or produce deformed flowers or fruit. Plants in which a virus has been diagnosed should be removed and destroyed so as to prevent the disease from spreading. Some viruses are spread by aphids, so elimination or prevention of these is some insurance against this disease.

Table 4 lists the more common fungal, bacterial and viral infections.

REMEDIES

Confusion often confronts the gardener attempting to buy the correct spray for the pest or disease to be controlled or eliminated. Some spray manufacturers name their range of products in a helpful way. For example, a remedy for snails might be called 'Kilsnale'. But this is not always the case. It is therefore advisable for the grower to have some knowledge of the *chemical group* to which the spray belongs rather than to purchase by trade name only.

For example, carbaryl is often used in different formulations to combat chewing insects. When buying this from a gardening shop, therefore, insist that the spray you want is based on a carbaryl formulation. The trade name is of little consequence.

To assist the grower in selecting the correct spray for his or her purpose, Appendix 6 lists the seven types of pests and diseases, the chemical group name of the remedies and some trade names.

By the intelligent use of Tables 3 and 4, in conjunction with Appendix 6, most of the pests and diseases likely to attack the plants can be eliminated or at least brought under control.

Notice that remedies 1, 2 and 3 in Appendix 6 are for broad, general groups; 4, 5, 6 and 7 are specifically for red spider, ants, slugs and whitefly respectively. Remedies 4 and 7 can also be used against sucking insects in general.

Snail bait is most effective when sprinkled evenly along the walls and paths around the growing beds. Do not place it directly on the growing medium.

Spraying

Most chemical sprays are toxic to humans, some more so than others. A little knowledge about the handling, storage, compatibility and toxicity of these potentially dangerous chemicals is therefore important. This will certainly ensure a more intelligent approach to spraying, with more effective results.

Most of the sprays mentioned in Appendix 6 may be purchased either as *emulsions* or as *wettable powders*. An emulsion is similar to milk – a suspension of very fine globules of oil in water. A *wettable powder* is a fine powder containing the active ingredient mixed with a wetting agent to ensure its even dispersion in water.

The object of spraying is to produce a very fine mist that will adhere to the leaves, particularly

Table 5: Summary of pests and diseases and their control		
A General pests	Chewing	Carbaryl or mercaptothion
	Sucking	Mercaptothion or chlorpyrifos
B Specific pests	Red spider	Thiophosphates or dicafol
	Ants	Gamma-BHC (Gamma-HCH)
	Slugs	Metaldehyde/carbaryl
	Whitefly	Synthetic pyrethroids, such as Cypermethrin
C Diseases	Fungal	Mancozeb and mixtures or Chlorothalonil or Benomyl
	Bacterial	Remove and destroy plants
	Viral	Remove and destroy plants

their undersides, and the stem of the plant. Insects are killed either on contact or after sucking the toxic spray. Some sprays are *systemic*, which means that they become part of the sap system, thereby rendering the whole plant toxic to sucking insects for two or three weeks.

It is worth repeating that most sprays are poisonous, especially in their concentrated form. If any is spilt on the skin, it should be washed off with water *immediately* and the affected parts rewashed with soap and water. Needless to say, all sprays should be kept locked in a safe place away from children, pets and foodstuffs.

In most countries, government regulations compel all spray manufacturers to state not only the chemical composition of the product, but also warnings on safe picking dates, common precautions on handling, mixing directions for use on various plants and compatibility with other spray types. In some cases symptoms of poisoning and antidotes are also mentioned.

In the United Kingdom it is illegal to use a product on a given crop unless this has been approved. The law has been tightened up considerably in recent years; many of the chemicals that were widely used cannot now be used at all. Others have been restricted. Lists of approved products are available, together with the crops on which they can be legally used. Further, the use of professionally approved chemicals by unlicensed amateurs is also illegal, with severe penalties.

Always read the labels thoroughly and adhere as closely as possible to the manufacturer's instructions regarding mixing. Remember that using the spray at a greater concentration than instructed may lead to damage and eventually even the death of the plants.

Some sprays are not compatible with others. If this is known to be the case, it will be necessary to spray with one type and complete the job with another.

Avoid spraying during windy or rainy weather. The best time is during the early part of the morning or late in the afternoon.

Establish the exact capacity of the reservoir of small hand-sprayers. With this knowledge, it is an easy matter to obtain the correct dilution called for in the instructions. For example, if the instructions on the label call for 10 ml (2 tsp) of a spray per 10 litres (2 gallons) water, and your sprayer has a 2 litre (3½ pint) capacity, you will have to use one-fifth of the 10 ml (2 tsp), that is, 2 ml (½ tsp).

One last warning: ALWAYS WASH VEGETABLES OR FRUITS THAT HAVE BEEN SPRAYED THOROUGHLY BEFORE EATING.

STERILIZATION OF GROWING MEDIUM

By the end of the growing season, disease-producing micro-organisms may have accumulated in the gravel or sand, increasing the risk of disease for any future crops. An end-of-season chemical sterilization is therefore recommended as standard procedure. (These remarks are particularly addressed to the growers of flowers, fruit or vegetables in hydroponic beds, although are also applicable to those growing on a smaller scale.)

Sterilization will certainly eliminate any soil- or water-borne micro-organisms introduced to the roots. This procedure can only take place after all the plants have been removed, since the chemicals used would severely damage root systems, eventually causing death.

Two chemical sterilants are in general use, namely, *formaldehyde* (which is banned in some countries) and *active chlorine*. The former, a gas, can be purchased as a 38 per cent solution in water, commercially known as *formalin*. The fumes of this material are extremely pungent, so it is important to take great care when handling.

For sterilization purposes, formalin is diluted 75 times (1,300 ml per 100 litres water [2 pints per 20 gallons]) thus producing a 5,000 parts per million concentration of formaldehyde. If using the gravel sub-irrigation method of hydroponics (see page 44), pour the recommended dosage of formalin into the reservoir, instead of the nutrient. After pumping this solution into the gravel, allow it to stand *overnight* and then drain to waste. After three successive water washings to remove all traces of formalin, the gravel, pump, pipelines and reservoir will have been effectively sterilized. Bear in mind that porous gravels will require at least one extra washing. Sterilization can be made more effective by covering the growing medium with a sheet of plastic.

Do not attempt to sterilize old vermiculite. Firstly, as it is so porous, it would be difficult to completely wash out the last traces of formalin. Secondly, this material would not be suitable for re-use in any case, as it is physically unstable.

Because of the problem of washing out the last traces of the sterilant, the overhead sterilization of a growing medium like sand is a far more difficult undertaking. Formalin is not recommended here but steam sterilization, a similar procedure used by soil-growers, is very feasible.

To effectively sterilize hydroponic beds with active chlorine, use a 70 per cent superchlorinated lime (as used in swimming-pools) dissolved in water at the rate of 1.5 kg per 1,000 litres (3 lb per 200 gallons) of water. Approximately, this makes a 1,000-parts-per-million solution of active chlorine. On a small scale, household bleach will serve the purpose.

It is essential to wash the medium thoroughly with water after sterilization has been completed.

CHAPTER ELEVEN

QUESTIONS AND ANSWERS

It seems that to some people hydroponics is shrouded in an aura of mystery. For example, some years ago the author was asked in a letter whether it was true or false that seed from hydroponically grown plants was sterile! Just why this strange notion should have arisen is hard to imagine, but the example serves to illustrate the kinds of misconceptions that exist!

Many other questions that are quite valid may well arise in readers' minds. In an attempt to anticipate some of these, we pose frequently asked questions and attempt to answer them.

Q.1 *Is hydroponics 'unnatural'?*

A. It all depends on what is meant by 'unnatural'. *The Shorter Oxford English Dictionary* defines the word as, 'Not in accordance with the usual course of nature; artificial'. We must answer the question in the light of this definition.

Before we do this, it is relevant to discuss briefly the two opposing schools of thought regarding the use of 'artificial' fertilizers in agriculture. On one side we have the *organic* growers and farmers who are opposed to the use of fertilizers other than those of organic origin, such as farmyard manure, compost, leaf mould and other 100 per cent organically based fertilizing materials. They allege that the so-called artificials are injurious to the soil, to the health and quality of the crops and consequently to the health and well-being of animals and humans. They claim to have evidence to suggest that 'artificial' fertilizers are chemical additives that eventually destroy microbial life in the soil and affect its fertility. This leads to crops poor in health and nutrition, hence also the animals feeding on these crops, and ultimately, humans living on both the crops and the animals.

The other school of thought – let us call it the *inorganic* school – agree that organically produced crops would be the ideal. However, in our modern world the amount of organic waste that can be recovered for use in agriculture is inadequate. Furthermore, the labour involved in collecting and applying these is too demanding to satisfy today's mechanized farming methods. There was no problem a century or two ago when the world population was smaller, and most of the food was consumed on the mixed farms and in neighbouring villages. A good deal of the plant nutrients was returned to the land as manure. Today the bulk of the food goes to the big cities and, after purification,

Ornamental plants grown under shelter

the resultant sewage is run into rivers or the sea.

The 'inorganic' school of thought holds that with the intelligent use of fertilizers, no harm is done to the soil, nor to the crops and animals feeding on them. But what is the scientific evidence for these claims?

John Bennet Lawes, a chemical manufacturer, and Joseph Henry Gilbert, a young chemist, began collaborating in 1843, in what has since been known as the Classical Plots of Rothamsted. Over 57 years, one of the longest scientific partnerships on record, they carried out epoch-making investigations that benefitted agriculture universally.

To this day, certain of the plots are given annual dressings of fertilizers. The soils have remained in good condition and continue to produce satisfactory crops. Careful counts have shown that there have been no negative effects on the earthworms and soil micro-organisms. Thorough investigations have failed to show that organic manures have any special effect, beneficial or otherwise, compared with balanced fertilizers.

A further point is that many soils have natural deficiencies in certain of the macro- and micro-elements. It follows that the crops, and consequently the crop residues and farmyard manure, tend to have the same deficiencies. Only by the application of fertilizers and trace elements can these be made good. In this way, large areas in many parts of the world, formerly useless for agricultural purposes, have been brought under cultivation. In short, without inorganic fertilizers we would not be able to feed the ever-increasing world population.

But to return to hydroponics, which is, after all, fertilizing taken to its logical conclusion. Soil is replaced by an inert growing medium. There are neither earthworms to kill nor microbes to poison, if indeed it is conceded that dilute fertilizer solutions do just this! The dilute soil solution derived largely from *inorganic* minerals found in the soil, is replaced by a scientifically balanced nutrient solution of similar composition.

In fact, similar inorganic constituents are absorbed by the root hairs (see Chapter Two), whether they are found in soil or provided by the nutrient solution. The same water is utilized by the roots, the same carbon dioxide extracted from the air by the leaves. The plant metabolizes in exactly the same way, producing flowers or fruit, 95 per cent of which are derived from water and carbon dioxide. Only 2–3 per cent of most plants are derived from the inorganic constituents found in soil.

We can therefore conclude that hydroponics is fully in accordance with the usual course of nature.

Q.2 *Do hydroponically grown vegetables have a 'chemical' flavour?*

A. With the greatest respect to those who have asked this question in all sincerity, it does seem rather naïve. The answer is an emphatic 'NO!'. In fact, providing that they are grown properly, hydroponic vegetables usually have a highly developed flavour. Bear in mind that the flavours of fruits and vegetables are also dependent on climatic conditions and not entirely on the method by which they are grown.

Flavour is derived from a mixture of secondary constituents including *essential oils, organic acids,* and *sugars.* All of these are produced during the natural metabolic process of the plant. Providing that similar and optimum conditions (for example, climate and pH levels) prevail during growth, the characteristic flavour of a tomato has no more connection with the nutrient solution supplied to the plant than the soil solution has to the same tomato grown in soil. Taste panels cannot distinguish between soil-grown and hydroponically grown tomatoes, although they are suffi-ciently acute to pick up taste differences between varieties grown by identical methods.

Without any doubt, hydroponically grown vegetables are extremely delicious and much sought after. Since smell and taste are closely linked, the same remarks apply to the scents of flowers.

Indeed, anyone suggesting that soilless-grown crops have a chemical flavour are without doubt imagining this.

Q.3 *What about the nutritional value of hydroponic vegetables?*

A. Extensive scientific research has been carried out on the nutritional content of tomatoes. The tomato is a fairly rich source of vitamin C, which is also found in many other vegetables and fruits.

Vitamin C is a metabolic product of a complex sugar derived from glucose as a result of photosynthesis. There is no significant difference in the amount of this vitamin produced in vegetables grown by soilless methods compared with the same vegetables grown in soil under similar climatic conditions. The mineral constituents – potassium, calcium, phosphorus, and so on – do show minor variations but, again, these are of no significance. Researchers in the United States have published scientific papers on this subject giving analyses of greenhouse tomatoes grown in soil and soilless media under exactly the same conditions. The results of this research show insignificant variations in mineral content.

The same conclusions apply to almost any vegetable grown hydroponically. Their quality and nutritional value show no significant differences from the same vegetables grown in a good soil.

Q.4 *Does hydroponics make out-of-season growing possible?*

A. Questions 1 and 2 perhaps provide a clue to the answer to this question. Unless greenhouse conditions with micro-climatic control are introduced, plants will no more easily be induced to produce crops out of season by hydroponic growing than they will in soil.

One possible significant benefit that hydroponic growing does enjoy is that cropping time is extended. But this should *not* be construed as out-of-season growing.

Q.5 *Can I grow really big tomatoes with hydroponics?*

A. This question really reflects that mystique attached to the word hydroponics'!

The short answer is 'No'. We should qualify this by saying that

The size of a tomato depends largely on the cultivar being grown

hydroponics has many benefits for the vegetable and flower grower, but this is not one of them.

The ultimate size of a ripe tomato, or any other fruit for that matter, depends mainly on the cultivar being grown. One can grow anything in size from the tiny *cherry* to the enormous so-called *beefsteak* or American hamburger.

Q.6 *Do I need a knowledge of chemistry for hydroponic gardening?*

A. No. For small-scale or amateur growing in hydroponic beds, commercial nutrient powders, which are

A small greenhouse is useful for home hydroponic growing

balanced and complete with trace elements, can be used. This renders chemical knowledge unnecessary.

Should the reader wish to compound a formulation, however, some knowledge of chemistry would be useful.

Commercial growing requires attention to detail as well as a commonsense approach to gardening. A working knowledge of plant physiology, pathology and chemistry will be useful, but is not essential.

Q.7 *Can mushrooms be grown by the hydroponic method?*

A. Unfortunately the answer is 'No'. Mushrooms belong to plant life known as fungi – relatives of the fungal diseases mentioned in Chapters Nine and Ten. As they do not have root, stem and leaf systems like other plants, their life cycle and metabolism are different.

Under conditions in which temperature, light and humidity are controlled, it is usual to grow mushrooms on straw or compost with

nutrients derived from manures. In The Netherlands, the UK, France, Germany, the USA, Canada, Thailand and India (and this list is not exhaustive!), extensive research into mushroom growing has been carried out. Many tonnes of mushrooms have been produced annually. But this is not strictly hydroponic growing.

Q.8 *How do hydroponic yields compare with those derived from soil-grown crops?*

A. Extremely favourably, although it has to be borne in mind that the best growers can achieve the same yields, irrespective of the methods used. The tomato is a good crop for making comparisons since it is frequently grown and we have an abundance of yield data on this plant. A realistic figure would be from two to four times the yield for hydroponics compared with field-grown tomatoes, although this will not necessarily be true for glasshouse-grown tomatoes.

In fairness we must state that the hydroponically produced tomatoes can be grown under protection, in the most favourable climatic conditions. Yields of over 300 tonnes per hectare (120 tons per acre) are not uncommon from the heated greenhouses of Europe. If we define 'yield' as the return of mass or numbers of fruit or flower per unit growing area per unit time, it should be apparent why hydroponic yields are usually superior.

The facts that plants are not in competition for available nutrients and hence can be planted closer to one another, and that they have shorter maturation periods, make for higher yields.

Q.9 *What exactly is 'tunnel' farming?*

A. This might also have been asked in another way, for instance: 'What are those tunnel-shaped plastic structures we sometimes see dotted over the countryside?'

Originating in France, and designed to protect plants from the cold European winters, the so-called tunnel is a framework made up of a series of metal pipes bent into a hemispherical shape and clad with a transparent plastic film of polythene. The ends of the tunnel have doors and provision is also made for ventilation flaps, which can be opened along the length of the tunnel.

The tunnels vary in length from about 25 to 100 m (27–110 yds), with 50 m (55 yds) being the average length. A typical width is about 8 m (19 yds) and height 3.5 m (11 ft). A continuous layer of plastic is laid along the floor, on to which are placed growing bags, with a 10–20 litre (2–4 gallon) capacity, in four to eight parallel rows. These are filled with sawdust, pine-bark or, sometimes, mixtures of these with peat, as the growing medium. Seedlings are transplanted into the bags, and,

There is always a demand for healthy seedlings

from an external reservoir, the medium is irrigated with a hydroponic nutrient mixture one or more times per day. Nutrient solutions are dripped into each growing bag from above by means of a system of micro-jets or fine 'spaghetti' tubing.

Many tunnel farmers use computer-controlled irrigation cycles.

A 50 m (55 yd) tunnel will accommodate approximately 1,100 tomato plants at a density of 2.75 plants per m² (2.3 plants per sq yd) and yield approximately 5–8 tonnes (tons)

A typical 'tunnel' showing hemispherical metal framework

per crop. With a double or inter-planted second crop over a total period of about fourteen months it is possible to realize a further yield of (3–5 tonnes) (tons). Obviously, these yields will depend on the length of growing season and location.

With English cucumbers, some 40–60 fruit (each measuring 300 mm [12 in]) per plant over a growing period of eight months can be expected. A 50 m (55 yd) tunnel will take about 800 plants.

Though generally practised by the commercial hydroponic grower, small single tunnels may also be used by the home grower.

Q.10 *Can I make money out of hydroponics?*

A. This is a very natural question and the answer is 'yes', providing that, as with any other business enterprise, you manage it efficiently. A few possibilities:

• Raising seedlings in vermiculite using the 'plug' system (see page 48) or growing cuttings in sand, vermiculite or perlite.

There is always a strong demand for healthy seedlings and cuttings. Here, on a modest scale, is an opportunity requiring an absolute minimum of capital. Even seeds such as indiginous wild flowers will germinate with ease.

• Growing the higher priced flowers in gravel or sand.

Flowers such as carnations, chrysanthemums or anthuriums, to name but three, usually fetch good prices on the floral market. Success depends very much on having the right outlets for their sale.

With a minimum of capital one can produce crops using the dry-feed system. This, however, is not as easy to control as gravel sub-irrigation, which requires the building of beds, reservoirs, the installation of pumps and, of course, a reasonable amount of capital.

• Growing indoor plants using the hydroculture method (see page 37).

There is a tremendous demand from shops, offices, house owners and flat-dwellers for indoor or orna-mental plants. Growing in leca has been described in detail (see pages 37–39). The scope for growing a variety of plants in different types of containers is endless. Bear in mind, though, that there are already large enterprises operating in this market.

• Growing nutritious salad crops.

There is always a demand for fresh, crisp vegetables such as cucumber, tomato, lettuce, peppers, celery and Swiss chard. Hydroponics certainly produces the quality!

Tunnel farming, discussed earlier in this chapter, affords definite possibil-ities for profit. Yields are excellent, the quality is superb, and the vegeta-bles can be presented in stretch-wrap plastic film. Hydroponically raised crops usually find a ready outlet at good prices through super-markets and other stores.

A word of caution here! Should you decide to grow for profit on a commercial scale you would be well advised to start out on a small scale in order to first develop a 'feel' for this fascinating method of growing.

Decorative indoor plants are always popular

CHAPTER TWELVE
HYDROPONICS AND THE FUTURE

Too often in the course of conversation on the subject, one hears the comment that hydroponics is something for 'the future'. But we pose the question: When does the future begin? *Today* was the future a decade, a generation or a century ago. While we glibly talk of 'the future', the years are swiftly passing us by. We believe that the future is *now*. Hydroponics is providing at this present time, and will continue to provide, at least a partial solution to the problem of feeding our world's population, which increases by 97 million per year.

THE WORLD'S POPULATION

The following table taken from *The Guinness Book of Records* shows estimates of the world population from AD 1800 to 2050.

Table 6

Date	Millions	Date	Millions
1800	954	1990	5,292
1900	1,633	2000*	6,261
1950	2,515	2025*	8,504
1980	4,450	2050*	10,019

* From UN Publication 'World Population Prospects 1990'

From the beginning to the end of the nineteenth century the world population increased by about 70 per cent; it is predicted that the

ISOSC (formerly IWOSC) arranges regular international congresses

increase for the twentieth century will be 280 per cent. The prospect of feeding these people, especially in the event of droughts and other natural disasters, is frightening. Even now, widespread famine and serious undernourishment are major problems in many parts of the world.

We must also consider the facts that extra housing has to be found and further industries established to accommodate all these people. This, in turn, means that less arable land will be available. At the present time this stands at 21 per cent of the world's land surface, though only 7.6 per cent is actually under cultivation.

How can hydroponics help? Firstly, arable soil is not a necessity, as any ground, sloping or flat, rocky or heavy with clay, can be used for producing crops.

Secondly, anything grown in soil can also be grown hydroponically. In practice, however, economic considerations often dictate what crops we can grow. Mainly vegetable crops have been mentioned in this book. While, in all conscience, these are vital to our health and nutrition, vegetables alone cannot sustain us.

STAPLE CROPS

Barley, wheat, rye, oats, maize, rice, potatoes and millet are perhaps the main cultivated crops on which the bulk of the world's population depends. To these we can add sugar, coffee, tea, cocoa and probably several other important agricultural products like cottonseed, sunflower and rape seed. All of these crops require large areas of arable land and, at the present time, are not cultivated by hydroponic methods, mainly for economic reasons.

It would be perfectly feasible, however, to grow any of these crops in sand, with computer-controlled irrigation. Even mechanically assisted dry-feeding is a possibility. Many modern-day fruit farmers utilize the overhead-drip system of irrigation to fertilize their fruit trees.

WATER AND CLIMATE

Provided that climatic conditions are favourable, and even here we can exercise some control, any edible crop can be cultivated.

Water for irrigation can be produced from our vast oceans

Water of suitable agricultural quality remains a limiting factor. Without water there can be no form of agriculture. But there is an answer. It is possible, at a price, to produce fresh water from sea water (see page 36). Water from the oceans is collectively estimated to weigh 1.3×10^{18} tonnes (tons). If a means could be devised to mechanically convey this, for example by pumping, to the growing area in which it is required, then water of suitable quality will always be available. Lakes and rivers are another possible source.

DESIGN FOR THE FUTURE

Architects could include in their designs of future flats and houses not only decorative built-in containers for indoor plants, but also garden hydroponic installations for raising fresh vegetables. The area at the top of blocks of flats or even garage roofs could also be utilized.

There is no reason why unutilized basement areas could not also be put to good use. However, artificial light would be essential, thus increasing production costs.

The auxiliary production of edible crops needs careful planning and co-ordination at government level. Demonstration centres would have to be set up and intensive training would also be necessary.

INTERNATIONAL SOCIETIES AND RESEARCH

The International Society for Soilless Culture (ISOSC) is one body devoted to the worldwide promotion of research and the application of soilless culture (see page 12); another is the International Society for Horticultural Science whose soilless culture division overlaps ISOSC to a certain extent. Both arrange international congresses where scientists meet to exchange ideas and to present their latest research work.

Many countries have established local societies with similar aims and objectives. Some of these are The Australian Hydroponic Association, The Association for Vegetables Under Protection in South Africa, The Hydroponic Society of America, and The International Centre for Special Studies in Hawaii. In addition, universities and agricultural research stations in most countries support active and ongoing research in hydroponics. For example, research at the Glasshouse Crops Research Institute, Littlehampton, England, was largely responsible for our knowledge of NFT.

One must not overlook the contribution of individuals working on their own initiative and expense. Several, especially those with an engineering background, have developed some novel hydroponic techniques.

CONTINUOUS LETTUCE PRODUCTION

The 'Hydroponic Lettuce Factory', which was designed and developed in Denmark, is an ingenious application for continuous lettuce production. In this machine, lettuces grow on a moving conveyor system under artificial light or natural light in a greenhouse. It can be set up anywhere and is very versatile in the sense that different methods of irrigation or different transport systems can be provided.

In another system that originated in The Netherlands, lettuces are planted into peat blocks placed in two parallel sets of holes made in 60 m (66 yd) lengths of polypropylene and grown in air-heated glasshouses. One end of the plastic is attached to a horizontal drum set at working height. An NFT system (see page 20) of growing in shallow troughs is used.

After two to three months, when the lettuces are ready for harvesting, four of these polypropylene growing strips containing eight closely

Hydroponic '6-day' fodder produced from maize

packed rows of lettuces are mechanically wound on to a drum where blades cut the lettuces clean away from the roots and peat blocks.

HYDROPONIC FODDER

The production from seed of nutritious green fodder within seven days is another interesting development that holds many benefits for stockbreeders and others concerned with raising animals. The main advantage of this system is that throughout the year, regardless of climatic conditions, fresh fodder can be produced on the farm, where it is needed. Growth is rapid and the nutritional value of the product excellent.

Briefly, the fodder 'factory' consists of a room some 8 m x 4 m x 2.5 m (25 ft x 12 ft x 8 ft). Temperature must be controlled and remain between 20 °C and 28 °C (68–83 °F) and artificial (fluorescent) lighting is necessary. The room houses a six-layered framework on which the growing trays are placed. These trays, made of plastic or aluminium, are only about 60 mm (2 in) deep. The seed of one of the cereal grains – oats, barley, maize or millet – is placed in a thin layer in the tray, thoroughly soaked with water, and left overnight. Germination soon takes place. The seed is sprayed with a dilute hydroponic nutrient solution two or three times each day and, after six or seven days, depending on the grain used, a delicious green mat about 150 mm (6 in) high will have grown. This is fed, roots and all, directly to the animals. After seeding one layer of trays each day, the grower harvests daily. This then becomes a continuous process.

The fodder 'factory' can produce some 500 kg (1,100 lb) of fresh green fodder from 50 kg (110 lb) seed *daily*.

ALGAL SOUP

An interesting sidelight on auxiliary food production is the mass cultivation of algae, very similar to the green scum seen growing on stagnant pools.

Algae are single-celled organisms containing chlorophyll, which photosynthesize in the same manner as leaves. Many different species exist, but one or two have been selected by plant scientists for the production of algal 'soup', which is rich in protein, fat, carbohydrates and vitamins A, B_1 and C. They are cultivated in large ponds containing nutrients similar to those used for growing land plants. The mature crop is harvested and dried for use as a supplement in the nutrition of animals and humans.

Publication 600 from the Carnegie Institute, Washington DC, USA, provides full details on algal cultivation.

INTO SPACE ...

Space stations are already with us. During the 80s and 90s we have seen a growing sophistication in the development of space stations of the future. Apart from the logistics of actually getting the station into space and keeping it there for extended periods of time, there is the problem of food. The National Aeronautics and Space Administration (NASA) has not been idle in this direction. Extensive research has produced 'The Salad Machine' – a hydroponic method for growing lettuce in space. This employs the irrigation technique of aeroponics (see page 22). Although the growing of lettuces presents no great problems on earth, two major technical problems had to be overcome before the system could work in space. These were weightlessness and the necessity to conserve a precious supply of onboard water. The latter problem was solved by purifying the wash water used by the crew and then recycling it in lettuce growing. Specially designed plastic sheets form the base on which the lettuces grow.

... AND BACK HOME

So, dear reader, we have completed our story and hopefully guided, perhaps even goaded, you into trying hydroponics. Why not go out and buy some seeds, a window-box, perhaps some vermiculite, and a small quantity of nutrient powder; and, who knows, maybe you too will be enjoying the sight of some petunias or the delicate flavour of a fresh, crisp lettuce before long?

Enjoy the sight of colourful flowers

APPENDIX 1
Conversion tables

Linear measure

Metric

10Å	= 1 mμ
1,000 mμ	= 1 μ
1,000 μ	= 1 mm
10 mm	= 1 cm
100 cm	= 1 m
1,000 m	= 1 km

Imperial

12 in	= 1 ft
3 ft	= 1 yd
1,760 yd	= 1 mile

Metric to Imperial

1 mm	= 0.03937 in
1 cm	= 0.3937 in
1 m	= 39.37 in / 3.281 ft / 1.094 yd
1 km	= 0.6214 mile

Imperial to metric

1 in	= 25.4 mm / 2.54 cm
1 ft	= 0.3048 m
1 yd	= 0.9144 m
1 mile	= 1.6093 km

Square measure

Metric to Imperial

1 cm²	= 0.1550 sq in
1 m²	= 10.764 sq ft / 1.196 sq yd
1 ha	= 2.4711 acres

Imperial to metric

1 sq in	= 6.4516 cm²
1 sq ft	= 0.0929 m²
1 sq yd	= 0.8361 m²
1 acre	= 0.40468 ha
1 sq mile	= 259 ha

Cubic measure

Metric to Imperial

1 cm³	= 0.061 cu in
1 m³	= 35.315 cu ft / 1.308 cu yd

Imperial to metric

1 cu in	= 16.387 cm³
1 cu ft	= 0.02832 m³

Capacity

Metric

1,000 ml	= 1 *l*

Imperial

20 fl oz	= 1 pt
8 pt	= 1 gal

Metric to Imperial

1 *l*	= 35.2 fl oz / 1.759 pts / 0.22 gal

Imperial to metric

1 fl oz	= 0.02835 *l*
1 pt	= 0.568 *l*
1 qt	= 1.136 *l*
1 gal	= 4.546 *l*

Mass

Metric

1,000 g	= 1 kg
1,000 kg	= 1 t

Imperial

437.5 gr	= 1 oz
16 oz	= 1 lb (avoir.)
112 lb	= 1 cwt
2,240 lb	= 1 ton (long)
2,000 lb	= 1 ton (short)

Metric to Imperial

1 kg	= 2.204 lb / 35.27 oz

Imperial to metric

1 oz	= 28.35 g
1 lb	= 453.6 g
1 ton (short)	= 0.90718 t
1 ton (long)	= 1.01605 t

Other useful conversions

1 t	= 2,204.62 lb
1 long ton of water	= 35.8 cu ft
1 gal of water	= 10.0 lb
1 imp. gal	= 1.20094 US gal
1 US gal	= 0.83268 British gal
1 cu ft	= 6.25 gal
1 short ton per acre	= 2.24 t per ha
Oz per gal x 6.25	= g per *l*
ppm	= lb per 100,000 gal or mg per kg
1 acre	= 4,840 sq yd or 43,500 sq ft
1 grain per gallon	= 14.3 ppm
°C	= ⅝ (°F -32)
°F	= ⅗ °C +32

Abbreviations used above

Å	Ångström unit	**m**	metre
cm	centimetre	**m³**	cubic metre
cm³	cubic centimetre	**mg**	milligram
cwt	hundred-weight	**ml**	millilitre
ft	foot/feet	**mm**	millimetre
g	gram	**Ml**	megalitre
gal	gallon	**mμ**	millimicron
gr	grain	**oz**	ounce
ha	hectare	**ppm**	parts per
in	inch		million
kg	kilogram	**pt**	pint
km	kilometre	**t**	tonne
l	litre		(metric)
lb	pound	**μ**	micron
		yd	yard

A splendid start for Aglaonema maria *plantlets*

APPENDIX 2

Trade name list of some products used in hydroponics

Bitumen emulsions:	'Autokote', 'Bituseal liquid', 'Flintkote'
Bitumen solutions:	'Bituprime', 'Shell', 'Sovacote 7094'
Conductivity meters:	'Jenco', 'Hanna', 'Volmatic'
Electric pumps:	'Calpeda', 'Induna', 'Jabsco', 'Yamaha', 'Ingersoll-Rand'
Fluorescent lamps:	'Gro-lux', 'Philips', 'Thorn', 'Wotan'
Incandescent lamps:	'Compton', 'GEC', 'Philips', 'Thorn','Wotan'

Greenhouse coverings:

Polythene and PVC	'Gundle', 'Soliflex', 'Uvidek'
Fibreglass	'Paxit'
Shadecloth	'Alnet', 'Knittex'
Polycarbonate	'Ampaglass', 'Modek'

Nutrient powders:

Single with trace elements	'Chemicult'
Two-part concentrate	'Chemicult K', 'Chemicult KX'
Perlite:	'Genulite', 'Pratley'
pH meters:	'Jenco', 'Hanna', 'Volmatic'

Time-clocks:	'Sangamo', 'Horstmann'
Tunnel structures:	'Gemcon', 'Greenzone'
Universal indicator:	'BDH', 'Johnson', 'Merck', 'Riedel de Hahn'

The above list of trade-names is by no means complete, nor is mention of a name an implied or intended endorsement of a product.

A variety of red lettuce in plastic gullies

APPENDIX 3

Commercial ingredients for mixing formulae

Element	Salt	Molecular formula
Nitrogen (Nitrate)	1 Potassium nitrate	KNO_3
	2 Calcium nitrate	$Ca(NO_3)_2 . 4H_2O$
	3 Sodium nitrate	$NaNO_3$
	plus 16	
Nitrogen (Ammonium)	4 Ammonium sulphate	$(NH_4)_2SO_4$
	5 Ammonium nitrate	NH_4NO_3
	6 Urea	
	plus 7 and 8	$CO(NH_2)_2$
Phosphorus	7 Ammonium dihydrogen phosphate (MAP)	$NH_4H_2PO_4$
	8 Di-ammonium hydrogen phosphate (DAP)	$(NH_4)_2HPO_4$
	9 Potassium dihydrogen phosphate	KH_2PO_4
	10 Monocalcium phosphate	$CaH_4(PO_4)_2 . H_2O$
	• common superphosphate	
	• food grade	
	• treble superphosphate	
	11 Phosphoric acid	H_3PO_4
Potassium	12 Potassium sulphate	K_2SO_4
	13 Potassium chloride	KCl
	plus 1 and 9	
Calcium	14 Calcium sulphate (Native gypsum)	$CaSO_4.2H_2O$
	plus 2 and 10	
Magnesium	15 Magnesium sulphate (Epsom salt)	$MgSO_4.7H_2O$
	16 Magnesium nitrate	$Mg(NO_3)_2.6H_2O$
Sulphur	17 From the Sulphates in 4, 10, 12, 14 and 15	

APPENDIX 4

Formula for 100 g (3 ½ oz) of trace elements

Element	Salt	Formula	Grams
Iron (Fe)	Ferrous sulphate	$FeSO_4.7H_2O$	78.0
Manganese (Mn)	Manganese sulphate	$MnSO_4.4H_2O$	7.8
Copper (Cu)	Copper sulphate	$CuSO_4.5H_2O$	0.8
Zinc (Zn)	Zinc sulphate	$ZnSO_4.7H_2O$	1.9
Boron (B)	Boric Acid	H_3BO_3	11.3
Molybdenum (Mo)	Sodium molybdate	$Na_2MoO_4.2H_2O$	0.2

APPENDIX 5

Four hydroponic nutrient formulae

Germany
Knop's Formula (1865) No. 1 — Grams per 100 *l*

Potassium nitrate	20
Calcium nitrate	80
Monopotassium phosphate	20
Magnesium sulphate	20
TEDM (or use 100 ml TEC; see page 35)	2
Total	142

United States of America
Summer Formula No. 2 — Grams per 100 *l*

Potassium nitrate	110
Calcium sulphate (gypsum)	76
Magnesium sulphate	52
Monocalcium phosphate (treble supers)	31
Ammonium sulphate	14
TEDM (or use 100 ml TEC; see page 35)	3
Total	286

United Kingdom
Formula No. 3 — Grams per 100 *l*

Potassium nitrate	55
Sodium nitrate	64
Monocalcium phosphate (treble supers)	44
Ammonium sulphate	12
Magnesium sulphate	52
Calcium sulphate (gypsum)	86
TEDM (or use 100 ml TEC; see page 35)	3
Total	316

Republic of South Africa
Formula No. 4 — Grams per 100 *l*

Calcium nitrate	135
Magnesium sulphate	55
Monocalcium phosphate (treble supers)	47
Ammonium sulphate	19
Potassium sulphate	75
TEDM (or use 100 ml TEC; see page 35)	3
Total	334

Formulae Nos. 1, 3 and 4 cannot be stored in the dry form owing to the hygroscopic (moisture absorbing) properties of calcium and sodium nitrate.

Built-in window-boxes, ideal for flat-dwellers

Commercial growing in leca

APPENDIX 6

List of pests and diseases with appropriate sprays

Problem	Chemical group name	Trade names
1a Chewing insects	Carbaryl 80% wettable powder	'Karbaspray' 'Kombat Worms'
b	'Mercaptothion 50% emulsifiable liquid	'Malasol' 'Malathion' 'Beetelsprey'
2a Sucking insects	As for 1b	As for 1b
b	Chlorpyrifos	'Chlorpyrifos' 'Dursban'
3a Fungal diseases	Mixture of Thiocarbamates wettable powder	'Dithane M45'
b	Chlorothalonil	'Bravo 500'
c	Benomyl	'Benlate'
4a Red spider and sucking insects	Systemic thiophosphate	'Rogor CE' 'Aphicide' 'Kombat Aphids'
b	Dicofol	'Kelthane AP'
5 Ants	Gamma-BHC (or Gamma-HCH) emulsifiable concentrate	'Dyant' 'Kombat Ants'
6 Snails & Slugs	Metaldehyde with or without carbaryl as pellets or liquid	'Sluggem' 'Disa' 'Snailban' 'Kombat Snails'
7 Whitefly	Synthetic Pyrethroids	'Ripcord' 'Sumicidin' 'Kombat Fruitfly'

Hazardous chemicals and their uses are strictly controlled by government regulations. As each country's laws will vary, please consult your horticultural advisor or follow the manufacturer's instructions carefully.

*Cucumber leaves infected with
downy mildew*

GLOSSARY

aerobic Living and functioning on air.

algae Lower form of plant life.

asexual Reproduction without sex.

bed The demarcated area in which plants grow.

bituminized Painted with bitumen.

break A side shoot.

calcareous Containing lime.

cellulose A complex carbohydrate, which is the most significant constituent of plant cell walls.

chlorophyll Green colouring matter in plants.

chlorosis Showing signs of yellowing.

conductivity A measure of the conducting capacity of water due to dissolved salts (see E.C).

cultivar Variety produced by cultivation (e.g. tomato).

cutting A side shoot from a plant used for cultivation purposes.

cytoplasm The main component of protoplasm.

dry-feed The application of nutrients in a dry form.

E.C. Electrical conductivity (see siemens).

emulsion A homogenous mixture of water and oil.

galvanized Coated with zinc.

gravel Rock material between 2 mm and 9 mm (⅛-½ in) in diameter.

gully A channel made of plastic for NFT growing.

humus Decomposed remains of plants and animals imparting blackness to soil.

hydroculture A system of growing indoor plants in clay pellets.

inorganic Of mineral origin, derived from non-living substances.

leca An acronym for 'light expanded clay pellets'.

macro-elements The six main plant nutrient elements.

medium The material in which plants grow, e.g. gravel, vermiculite.

metabolism Process whereby the plant builds up nutritive material or breaks down complex into simpler substances.

micro-jet A device for distributing small controlled volumes of liquid.

micro-elements Nutrient elements required in trace amounts.

microsiemens One-millionth of a siemens (see E.C.).

millisiemens One-thousandth of a siemens (see E.C.).

NFT Acronym for 'Nutrient Film Technique'.

nutrient A mixture of macro- and micro-elements that are vital to plant growth.

organic Derived from living substances.

osmosis The passage of a liquid through a semi-permeable membrane.

perlite A mined mineral of volcanic origin used as a growing medium.

pH (value) Measure of acidity or alkalinity of a solution.

photosynthesis Production of sugars by leaf chlorophyll in sunlight.

protoplasm Life-giving fluid filling plant cells, differentiated into cytoplasm and nucleoplasm.

relative humidity Percentage of water vapour in the atmosphere compared with a saturated atmosphere at the same temperature.

reservoir Container for nutrient solution.

respiration Taking in oxygen and exhaling carbon dioxide (cf. breathing in humans).

rockwool A material made by heating diabase (a rock), coke, and limestone in a furnace at 1,600 °C (2,880 °F).

sand Soil material between 0.25 mm and 2 mm (¹⁄₆₄-⅛ in) in size.

siemens The basic unit of conductivity (see E.C.).

soilless culture Popularly used synonomously with 'hydroponics'.

stock solution A concentrated aqueous solution to be diluted before use.

stomata Tiny apertures mainly on leaf's underside.

stopping Removal of growing point.

sub-irrigation Irrigation from below.

sump A small temporary reservoir.

systemic Entering a plant's system or cell sap.

tank See 'bed'.

transpiration Evaporation of water through stomata (cf. perspiration in humans).

tunnel Plastic-clad, semi-circular metal framework used as a greenhouse.

vermiculite Mined micaceous mineral processed for use as a growing medium.

A stand of healthy 'tunnel' cucumbers

SELECT BIBLIOGRAPHY

BOOKS

Bentley, Maxwell. *Hydroponics Plus*, Oregon, Timber Press, 1985

Cooper, Allen J. *The ABC of NFT*, London, Grower Books, 1979

Cooper, Allen J. *Nutrient Film Technique of Growing Plants*, London, Grower Books, 1976

Ellis, C. and Swaney, M.W. *Soilless Growth of Plants*, 2nd edn, New York, Reinhold Publishing Corp., 1953

Haubridge. G. (ed.) *Hunger Signs in Crops*, Washington, D.C., Judd Deitweiler.

Harris, Dudley. *Hydroponics: The Complete Guide to Gardening without Soil*, London, New Holland Publishers, 1987

Jones, J. Benton. *A Guide for the Hydroponic and Soilless Culture Grower*, Oregon, Timber Press, 1985

Jones, Lem. *Home Hydroponics and How to Do It*, Arizona, Beardsley Publishing Co., 1975

Resh, Howard M. *Hydroponic Food Production*, California, Woodbridge Press, 1981

Savage, Adam J. (ed.) *Hydroponics Worldwide: A State of the Art in Soilless Crop Production*, Honolulu, International Center for Special Studies, 1985

Schwarz, M. *Guide to Commercial Hydroponics*, Israel, Israel University Press, 1968

Sholto Douglas, J. *Advanced Guide to Hydroponics*, London, Pelham Books Ltd, 1976

Sholto Douglas, J. *Beginner's Guide to Hydroponics*, London, Pelham Books Ltd, 1972

Sholto Douglas, J. *Hydroponics – The Bengal System*, Oxford, Oxford University Press, 1975

The U.K. Tomato Manual, London, Grower Books, 1973

Selected papers from ISOSC world congress proceedings
1973, Sassari, Sardinia

J. Sholto Douglas, 'Nutrient film layflats; a low capital-cost technique for commercial hydroponics', 107

D.A. Harris, 'Commercial hydroponic fodder growing in South Africa', 75

F. Penningsfeld, 'Suitability of expanded plastics for hydroponics', 129

G. Rivoira *et al*, 'The use of slow release fertilisers in hydroponics', 195

M. Schwarz, 'The influence of balanced nutrient solutions and CO_2 under high saline conditions, 209

M. Schwarz, 'The use of waste water (sewage) in gravel culture', 219

A.A. Steiner, 'The selective capacity of tomato plants for ions in a nutrient solution', 43

1976, Las Palmas, Canary Islands

A.J. Cooper, 'Crop production with nutrient film technique', 121

D.A. Harris, 'A modified drip-culture method for the commercial production of tomatoes in vermiculite', 85

L.A.J. Lamers, 'Hydroponic gardens in offices', 57

H.M. Resh, 'A comparison of tomato yields using several hydroponic methods' 171

A.A. Steiner, 'The development of soilless culture', 21

M. Tropea, 'The controlled nutrition of plants II – A new system of "vertical" hydroponics', 75

F.L. Verwer, 'Growing horticultural crops in rockwool and nutrient film', 107

1980, Wageningen, Holland

J.M. Barrow, 'Hydroponic culture of grapes in the tropics', 443

R.D. Bliss, 'The Baguley system of drip hydroponics', 457

G.S. Davtyan, 'Classification of hydroponic methods of plant production', 45

P. Heymans, 'The development of the Argex/Leca clay pellets', 307

G. Magnani and F. Massantini, 'Hydroponic fodder growing; use of cleaner-separated seeds' 555

F. Massantini, '"Agriperlite" sacks: A new system of hydroponics', 469

F. Penningsfeld, 'Growing orchids in expanded clay', 313

J.B. Rankin, 'The use of sawdust as a growing medium for all crops in grow boxes in Central Africa', 385

E. Ruthner, 'All-year-round continuous crop production', 501

C. Sonneveld, 'Growing cucumbers and tomatoes in rockwool', 253

W.W. Tresise, 'Simple soilless culture for home gardens', 379

M. Tropea, 'The control of strawberry plant nutrition in the sack culture', 477

F.L. Verwer and J.J.C. Welleman, 'The possibilities of Grodan rockwool in horticulture', 263

1984, Lunteren, The Netherlands

A.C. Biggs and R.S. Donnan, 'Horticultural Rockwool – Australian experiences', 183

D.A. Harris and P.C.J. Maree, 'Growing tomatoes in a plastic greenhouse in uncomposted pine bark', 245

H. Enzerink and H.S. Huisman, 'Hydroculture for the decoration of houses, offices and hospitals', 203

J.C.J. Kuiken and E. van Os, 'Mechanisation of lettuce growing in nutrient film technique', 483

E.S. Lim and C.K. Wan, 'Growing vegetable crops in pots containing gravel chips by the recirculating flow technique under tropical conditions', 751

E.S. Lim and C.K. Wan, 'Vegetable production in the tropics using a two-phase substrate system of soilless culture', 317

P.C.J. Maree, 'Growing seedless English cucumbers in fresh pine sawdust and bark', 355

C. Sonneveld and G.W.H. Welles, 'Growing vegetables in substrates in the Netherlands', 613

A.A. Steiner, 'The universal nutrient solution', 633

H. Suzuki, 'The sandponics cultivation system' 651

F.L Verwer and J.C.C. Welleman, 'The latest developments on GRODAN rockwool for floriculture', 763

O. Verdonck *et al*, 'Argex – An expanded clay used as a substrate in hydroponics', 705

1988, Flevenhof, The Netherlands

K. Bartkowski and O. Nowosielski, 'The use of tray container technique (TCT) for industrial greenhouse tomato production' 83

K.D. Gruber and F. Penningsfield, 'The use of seawater for soilless culture', 385

D.A. Hall *et al*, 'Perlite culture: A new development in hydroponics', 177

P.C.J. Maree and J.M. Wyrley-Birch, 'Fly ash as a trace element source in soilless culture', 311

B. Vestergaard, 'The hydroponic lettuce factory', 449

A. Vincenzoni, 'Application of soilless culture for producing pepinos', 465

1992, Rustenburg, South Africa

F.-G. Schröder, 'Plant plane hydroponics, a new hydroponic system', 375

A.A. Steiner, 'Hydroculture for decoration in offices, hospitals and houses', 399

J.C.C. Welleman, 'Grodan substrate systems in the sub-tropics', 465

Bibliography on Soilless Culture, 1970 to 1983, Wageningen, ISOSC, 1984
Bibliography on Soilless Culture, 1984 to 1989, Wageningen, ISOSC, 1990
Bibliography on Soilless Culture, 1990 to 1991, Wageningen, ISOSC, 1992

Copies of the above papers and bibliographies are obtainable from:
The Secretariat of ISOSC, P.O. Box 52, 6700 AB, Wageningen, The Netherlands.